PATH BENEATH THE SEA

PATH
BENEATH
THE SEA

A NOVEL

BY DEVORAH OMER

TRANSLATED FROM THE HEBREW

BY ISRAEL I. TASLITT

A SABRA BOOK

FUNK AND WAGNALLS

NEW YORK

© 1969 AMERICAN-ISRAEL PUBLISHING COMPANY, LTD.
LIBRARY OF CONGRESS CATALOG CARD NUMBER 69–13469
PRINTED IN ISRAEL

For Uri and his friends,
whose experiences served
as background for this book

D.O.

One

I was born in Algeria, but I don't remember much about my native land. My family moved to Fez, a city in Morocco, while I was still a child. The only thing that stuck to me from the land of my birth was my Algerian name—Taboul.

This name, very popular in Algeria, later gave me a lot of trouble. At that time, though, I was still a boy, belonging to a well-to-do family. I had six sisters, all of them older.

I was the only son and my father had so wanted a son! In Morocco, any man who has no son is looked upon as being childless, no matter how many daughters he has. My mother knew this, and she really felt guilty towards my father.

"Another birth," the doctors told her, "will endanger your life."

But Mother wanted a son. She felt she had to give my father the son for whom he yearned. And so, I was born; and on that same day, my mother died. I became more than just a son; to my father I was *the* son.

Father had high hopes for me. He could hardly wait for me to finish high school and join him as a partner in his dry-goods store. But I always said: "When I grow up, I'll go to Israel and become a diver."

Why should the heart of a boy in Morocco be set on such a strange ambition? The diving part came perhaps from the antics of the older boys at the port, who dived for coins thrown by tourists from ships. As for Israel—well, I heard a lot about Israel from my sisters. They all belonged to some Zionist group and kept talking about Israel.

Funny, as I think of it now, one after another, they married and raised families—but not one of them ever got there.

But their chatter about it, around the dinner table, stayed with me. Then, too, I happened to see a movie about the adventures of frogmen. I don't remember the name of the film, but I recall, very clearly, all the scenes—the water becoming dark blue as the diver went deeper and deeper; the black diving suit and the eyes gleaming behind the bubble, the gliding movements, the struggle with the enemy, the attaching of a mine to the enemy's ship.

A frogman looked to me like a superman, and that's when, I think, I decided to be a frogman—just like the hero!

Father loved me—in his own way. He never showed any signs of affection; he didn't spoil me, that's certain. He was very strict and expected a great deal of me. Once I had made my decision, I had the feeling that he was sizing me up, wondering what would become of me, whether or not the life my mother gave, in order to give me life, was really worth the sacrifice.

One after another, my sisters left the house, until only the two of us remained, my father and I, plus Rosa the housekeeper, who came in the morning and left at night. I respected my father greatly; everyone in the city did. At the same time, I was really afraid of him, and this was not only because of the beatings he gave me (he believed in the saying, "Spare the rod and spoil the child"—and he never spared the rod).

It wasn't surprising that he didn't want to hear anything about my dreams of becoming a frogman in Israel— it was as though I had said the silliest thing imaginable. I used to bring it up every once in a while, then gave up. I knew that Father would never agree to it. I had no choice but to wait until I'd be twenty-one, when I'd be on my own and could do as I pleased. At the time, I was sixteen and very impatient about waiting so long.

Those were the days of the Sinai Campaign, in 1956. I read, with great excitement, all about the wonders of the Jewish army. I admired its courage. I already wanted to be there, in Israel, across the sea, a proud Jew. Here, in Morocco, Jews were not liked, especially the rich among them. And now that "our" forces routed the Egyptian army, the hatred toward the Jews went beyond all bounds.

I tried again to sound my father out about going to Israel, but his frown was enough to make me hold my tongue. The words simply never got beyond my lips. This time I knew that I must never bring up the subject again; father would never give his consent.

A few months later, a group of boys and girls in the Zionist club began to get ready to go to Israel, as a farm training unit. I envied those in the group, but I couldn't be one of them. "Without parents' approval, we don't take anyone," the leaders said.

Parents' approval? How was I going to get *that?*

It was the third day of winter. I remember it as though it were yesterday. Rain was falling without let-up, and I was in a miserable mood. On the following day the group was to set out for the port, on its way to Israel. This was my last chance. The form that my father had to sign had been in my pocket for many days, worn and wrinkled. Time and again, I had taken it out, looked at it, even tried to hand it to my father—but I didn't dare. And now, if I didn't do it today, they would leave without me, and I would have to wait until I became an adult—so many years away!

My thoughts, on that day, became increasingly bleak. What should I do? Should I simply run away? They wouldn't take me along. What if I hid in the hold of the ship? But how could I do it? And what if I were caught? More than anything else, I dreaded my father's wrath.

That day my mind wasn't on my studies at all. I was confused and desperate. I watched the rain trickling down the window panes and felt like crying. If only I had a mother! She would surely help me; mothers always help their children. I had never felt like an orphan, before this. I never knew my mother, nor did I feel any need for one. But on that winter day my eyes filled with tears at the thought of how simple everything would be—if I only had a mother, as did all the other children.

"Taboul!" the teacher's voice broke into my painful thoughts. The class was laughing. "Taboul, I called you by name five times! What is occupying your mind, dear child?" His face was like a storm cloud.

"I . . . well, no . . . that is," I stammered. "What *should* be occupying my mind, sir?" I blurted out, desperately.

I returned home with one cheek still smarting from the slap it had received. In my school bag there was a note for my father, written in an angry scrawl and sealed angrily in a stiff white envelope. This certainly was not the day for me to try arousing my father's goodwill.

Father was already out of sorts when he stepped into the house. He never was good-natured to begin with, but this time he kept pacing back and forth like an enraged animal. The teacher's note I handed him, to read and sign, didn't help matters, and the bad weather bothered his rheumatism. And as if that were not enough, an important shipment of goods he had been expecting was overdue. My palm, grasping the consent form, was wet with excitement and quivering with fear. Darkness came quickly, that cloudy evening, and my spirits were no lighter. The group was to leave the next morning at five, before dawn; I had only twelve hours left. If I didn't make my move now, everything would be lost. I would have to wait—but the thought of waiting all those years was enough to send a shudder through me.

Both of us—Father and I—ate our supper in complete silence, each lost in his own thoughts. Outside the rain kept coming down. Rosa removed the dishes from the table, washed them and came to bid us good night. "I won't be coming tomorrow before afternoon," she said as she was leaving. "I have an appointment with the dentist."

"Looks like they won't bring the goods any more," my father muttered. "I'm going to bed."

Lost, everything was lost! By the time Father would be up, the group would be on its way to Israel—without me.

It was already late. The large brown clock in the dining room had long ago struck the midnight hour. I couldn't sit still or do my lessons or fall asleep. Clasped in my hand was the wrinkled form. I knew what was in it by heart:

"I hereby affirm that I agree that my son/daughter should join the *Binyan and Aliya* training group which is leaving for Israel on the 'Mediterranean,' the purpose of this group being to become part of Israel's society by setting up a farm training unit in a kibbutz.

Signed...................."

The blank spaces stared me in the face. Father would never sign it, never. I was sure of this, horribly sure. The rain kept coming down; it had been pelting the roof since morning. Thunder rolled from the skies into the high wind that swept the city, with a noise that sounded like furniture being moved somewhere upstairs.

Maybe I should forge the signature? For a moment I played with the thought but then I dropped it. That would be a criminal trick which could easily land me in jail. "The end justifies the means," Amos, the counselor from Israel, once said. Did it mean that if I wanted to go to Israel, I had the right to do everything? I knew my father's signature very well. Why hadn't I thought of it before?

Suddenly I thought I saw a face in the window. When I looked again, it was gone. Then I heard steps shuffling outside, followed by an impatient rap with the brass door-knocker. Who could it be, at ten minutes to two? I tiptoed to the door, held my breath and listened.

"*Hawaja! Hawaja!*" I heard a voice in Arabic. It sounded familiar.

"Who's there?" I asked.

"Salim," answered the voice from behind the locked door. "Open quickly, *hawaja!*"

I opened the door. Salim was one of my father's trusted employees. "They brought the goods just now," he said. "They say there was a flood on the way. The truck got stuck and they couldn't come any earlier. Now they're here and they want to get a signature. Will you sign, young *hawaja?*"

"No," I pushed away the papers he wanted to give me. "I can't sign for Father. I wish I could," I added with a sigh, as I caught Salim's look of surprise. "Father will be very angry." My mind was very busy figuring out what would anger him most—if I'd sign his name, wake him up to sign, or send Salim away without any signature. I knew he would be angry in any case. He could fly off the handle at any little thing. I was trying to think which would be the least unpleasant course.

"Don't worry about it," advised Salim. "Don't put

on the light, so that the *Hawaja* won't wake up entirely. Just let him sign here, here and here, and go back to sleep."

"Good, good," I answered. Suddenly an idea hit me. I remember how Yaffa had gotten her parents' consent for that summer trip. At the time, I thought she did a terrible thing, I was even surprised that she would have done it. But now—I really wanted to go to Israel!

"Wait here," I told Salim and hurried off to my room. The consent form was in my desk, exactly where I had left it when I thought I saw someone peering in through the window. I picked it up. My hand was shaking and I could feel my knees rattling. I slipped the form in among the papers Salim had brought, and left the room. Father would either sign all the papers, or . . . I didn't dare think of what would happen if father discovered that I tried to trick him into signing. I felt a deep shame, my feet dragged along the suddenly-long corridor to my father's room. I opened the door and stepped into the dark room. From the direction of Father's bed, came a sound of light snoring. For a moment I was stricken dumb with fear. Finally, I opened my mouth and said, in an odd sort of voice: "Father, pardon me; Salim's here, he wants you to sign . . . for the shipment."

"What's the matter?" Father got up to one elbow. I was glad the darkness hid the flush of shame on my face. No, I couldn't do it. My fingers fumbled about for the crumpled form. I slipped it out and put it into my pocket at the moment my father turned on the light, and I handed him the papers to be signed. He groped about the small night-table and picked up his glasses and pen.

"So, you've been up waiting for the shipment?"

I didn't say anything. Father was suddenly very proud of me. "You'll grow up, Taboul," he said, giving me a warm look. "I'll change the sign. Instead of 'Cohen's Fabrics', it will read 'Cohen and Son', eh?"

"Father," I sat down on the bed, hopefully. This could be the right moment. "Father, I want to ask something of you."

"Go ahead," he said, his features suddenly calm. "What's the matter?"

"Father, you know that—."

"Go on, son,"

"I want to go to Israel . . . I—."

Father's face turned crimson. He sat upright, and his eyes blazed with fury. "I am offering you a partnership in the business, and you—you want to leave me?!"

"Father—."

"Silence! I'll never let you leave me! As long as I'm alive, you'll be right here, at my side! Do you hear me? Is this the thanks I get for everything I've done for you? You are heartless! I won't consent to this—ever! Do you hear?"

Two

The light in Father's room went out. Salim left with the signed papers, but I couldn't fall asleep. It was past two in the morning; I would be worn out. My lessons were not done. I was bound to have no end of trouble in school. Tomorrow all my friends would be far from the city and aboard ship, on their way to Israel, while I would remain here, forever.

I won't remain behind! I made my decision. I will go! Father refuses to sign—let him not sign! I'll get aboard ship and stow away. Yes, that's exactly what I'll do! I now felt much better. All I'd have to do was catch the first bus to the port. I'll get up to the deck and hide— that's what!

There was little time and much work to be done. I began packing my valise. I knew I couldn't take along very much; I would have to carry the valise all the way and conceal it where I'd be hiding. I threw in a few pairs of underwear, several shirts and trousers; it was more difficult to decide what to leave behind. My room was full of things I loved very much: my large stamp collection, my coin collection, photo albums, letters, books. A boy in a well-to-do home has many nice things, and these I now had to leave.

I knew where I was going. I also knew that my father would be very angry and might even break off with me. He would never allow these things to be sent to me in Israel. I took a few photographs out of the album—the family, my sisters, father. Before I closed the lid, I also put in my mother's picture, in its copper frame, which always stood on my desk. I locked the valise, sat down at the desk and wrote a note:

Dear Father,

When you read this, I shall be far from here, on my way to Israel. Forgive me, father, it couldn't be otherwise. That is where I belong. That's where I want to live. I hope that you will understand and that, some day, you will join me. Farewell. Your Taboul.

I sat for a while, looking at the note, then I drew my pen through the last line and added, in its place: "Your loving son, Taboul." I knew that this would not ease his anger but I felt that I had to do it, to be a little gentler. I did it not for the stern father whom I feared so much, but for the lonely old man whom I was leaving behind. I knew that he didn't want to let me go because of the bond that tied me to him. But my desire to be in Israel was stronger than anything else in the world.

I wrote another note to Rosa:

Dear Rosa:

In this envelope you'll find another envelope for my father. Give it to him as late as possible—only when he will begin to worry about me. I know I can depend on you. I shall write you soon and explain everything. Yours, with love, Taboul.

I placed the letter to my father in an envelope and wrote his name on it. I folded the envelope and inserted it, together with the note to Rosa, into a second envelope, on which I wrote Rosa's name in huge letters. I went down to the kitchen and looked for a spot to put it, where Rosa would see it before my father would. Rosa's blue apron was folded neatly in a drawer, ready to be put on in the morning. I thrust the letter into the apron pocket and shut the drawer. That was it. Now everything was in order.

I was hoping that Rosa wouldn't open her envelope in my father's presence, at breakfast. It wouldn't do for him to discover my flight that soon. The later he learned about it, the better would be my chance of reaching Israel.

I picked up the valise and tiptoed toward the door. I looked back for the last time: the solid dark furniture, the soft Persian rug . . . this home that I was now leaving behind in the hope of finding a new and better one, or perhaps one not as comfortable and prosperous, but still, a home in Israel, among Jews. At that moment I couldn't imagine that a new home is something you have to fight for, to build it, and that the fight is not an easy one.

No, I didn't know it—but even if I did, I wouldn't have retreated. I wanted to go to Israel, to be a diver in the Israeli navy, and I was prepared to make any sacrifice demanded of me. I turned the light off. The house was now completely dark.

"Good-bye, Father," I whispered. "Forgive me. I cannot do otherwise." I suddenly felt a deep love for

Father, the stern and lonely man whom I was now making lonelier many times over. But my happiness seemed to me, at that moment, to be the most important thing in the world.

The hands on my watch pointed to ten minutes before ten a.m. I crouched in the rear of the lower deck, looking nervously at the watch. If they would only weigh anchor and sail! Everything had gone so remarkably well—getting into the port area and going up the gangway. No one asked any questions. My hiding place was quite safe. I sat there and waited, tense and excited. When would they sail?

Suddenly I remembered something: Rosa! She wasn't coming in at her usual hour. Yesterday she told us that she would be going to see the dentist. How could I have forgotten it? Father would be very angry, if I weren't there to give him his coffee; whenever Rosa wasn't there, it was my job to do her work. Father didn't like to eat breakfast alone. Suppose he decided to look in the drawer. Did I really put the note into her apron pocket? Suddenly I wasn't sure. I was so tired and confused, my head was aching. And what if he found the letter? True, it was addressed to Rosa, but he might recognize my handwriting and open the envelope. He wouldn't let me go and they would take me off the ship.

I didn't budge from my hiding place all day. I was cold and hungry. What a fool I was, not to have taken some food from home! Why hadn't I thought of it? My hands and feet were so stiff, I couldn't feel them at all. I was terribly thirsty. Now I was sorry that it

had stopped raining; I could have moistened my lips with the drops. How long could I hold out?

Time passed at a maddening, slow pace. I tried not to look at my watch every few minutes. It would be better to take a look only once in a great while and see that a long time had really gone by. The ship was rolling lightly and I felt a slight nausea, caused by the motion or perhaps by my hunger and thirst. Then, too, I was worn out; this was my second night without sleep. Still, I was afraid that if I fell asleep, I would be discovered. But my eyes refused to stay open and weariness finally overcame me.

When I awoke it was already light. A rough-looking sailor was shaking me: "What the devil are you doing here?" he shouted.

What was I doing there? I had to tell the whole story to the sailor, then to the ship's officer and finally to the Captain.

"We'll set you down in Majorca when we get there, tomorrow evening," the Captain said sternly.

"Please don't!" I begged.

But he didn't want to listen, and I was almost ready to give up when an angel came to my rescue—Amos. Good Amos! I knew that he wouldn't desert me!

I don't know how Amos did it. While the ship was anchored in Majorca, my heart kept pounding with fear and agony. Finally, as the anchor was raised and the ship's course set toward the open sea, I began to breathe more freely. "The Lord be praised! I'm still here! I'll get to Israel!"—thanks to Amos.

Still, though I now felt I had pulled through, and that

I would go to Israel, my heart was filled with doubt and worry. I couldn't stop thinking of what must have been happening back home. By this time Rosa must surely have given the letter to my father. What would he do? Amos did promise to take care of me, but if Father would demand my return, even Amos would be powerless to help me. Would Father do this? Perhaps my action would convince him

I wished he would go and live with one of his daughters. I really prayed for it. He was strong but he feared loneliness. It's not easy for a father who had reared seven children, to find himself suddenly alone and abandoned. But at the same time, I was almost afraid of what he might do. He might cable the ship and demand that I be put ashore. But I won't let myself be! If they try it, I'll jump overboard and swim away. I must get to Israel! I must!

The ship kept on going, heading east.

We finally got there. I can't describe my feelings when I first saw the crest of the Carmel, through the morning mist. This is how a man, dying of thirst, must feel, when he comes upon the life-saving oasis in the desert. I may sound poetic, but that is how I felt that morning. I cried, unashamed.

There we were, forty-three boys and girls of sixteen. Burdened with bundles, packages and valises, we dreamily took our first steps on Israeli soil. That same day we traveled to the kibbutz where we would live, work and become a solid unit, then enlist in the preparation program for Nahal.

Nahal—I heard the term for the first time. When

I found out what Nahal was, I was deeply disappointed. "I want to be a diver," I protested.

"We'll have time to talk about it," said Amos. He was busy making the necessary arrangements for the trip to the Negev. But still, I was disappointed.

This was not the only disappointment that day. The Negev gave me an odd, depressive feeling. It was a dry winter, following a hard summer. All about the kibbutz, which rose out of the wilderness, was the yellow, barren desert. It looked unreal, as though a child had put up a few building blocks in the sand and stuck some green boughs among them.

Disappointments now followed one after the other. We had been warned that it wouldn't be easy, but we were not prepared for such hardships. All of us came from wealthy homes, children of doctors, lawyers, merchants. This transition from Father's beautiful and spacious home to a room in a shack with bare walls and four cots covered with gray woolen blankets was not very inspiring. But we were still full of excitement, ready for anything.

We went out for our first day's work—weeding the vegetable patch—in high spirits. But we soon discovered that it was much easier to sing about labor than to work and sing. An hour later my back was aching terribly, and my palms were covered with blisters. The future looked altogether different from what I had imagined.

Our program called for us to work half a day and spend the other half studying—Hebrew, Zionism, Bible, and so on—but, just at that time, the kibbutz was suffering from a shortage of working hands, and we were kept working all through the day. Any boy who had never worked in his life would find it hard to get used to, all at once—an eight-hour working day. The Negev sun was broiling. One day I went to work dressed only in a pair of shorts, and my entire body was badly burned.

"Everything is tough," said Amos, who had a motto ready for every occasion. If I ever had any doubt that mottos are based on facts, this beginning of mine dispelled it.

After the first week, my companions began getting letters from home. Everybody received mail—except me, of course. I waited for one, desperately checking the pile of mail every day. It took me a few weeks to realize that I really shouldn't be expecting any letters. I did write—the very first day, then again and again. Slowly it dawned on me that my father probably didn't even read my letters. Even if he did overcome his feelings and did take a glance, just to see how I was doing, he would never admit it by answering. I had hurt him deeply, as the head of the family, and this was something I felt he would never forgive. I then decided to write to Rosa, at her home address. I heard from her a week later.

Her letter gave me no cause for gladness. Rosa told me that my father received a shock when he heard that I had gone to Israel, despite his forbidding. She described how he had lowered his head to the table and cried. My big strong father had cried like a baby: "I had an only son, and he is gone." I felt the words coming at me from the letter, written in Rosa's slow, careful handwriting: "You are regarded here as being dead. Your name is not to be mentioned in his presence. 'I have no son,' he says. 'I had one and he is gone.' As your letters come, he throws them immediately into the fireplace. He won't let me read them to him, nor to note down your address. He has also forbidden your sisters to write you or to have any contact with you. 'Only the devil has contact with the dead,' he says . . . It's raining heavily here; we haven't had such a winter for many years. We had a large engagement party last week. Yaffa is engaged, and I find the couple to be very handsome."

I held on to the envelope and wanted to cry. All day I kept myself in check, but at night, when everyone was asleep, I let go. I don't recall having cried that way, ever since I was a small child. I had no father, no family, not anybody. I wept because Yaffa had become engaged. Why did she have to? And here I was, longing for her so deeply! But I wept because of other things, too. I was disappointed in everything—in myself, most of all. The hard life was killing me. I couldn't stand the meager kibbutz food. The monotonous work in the vegetable patch bored me terribly; I had hardly begun working on one patch, when the weeds would already crop up again in the one before it. But it wasn't only bodily pain. Our group was a sort of Moroccan island in the Israeli kibbutz. We continued talking French; we hardly made any progress in Hebrew, since we had not been given very much instruction. We couldn't relate to the kibbutz people, who were our seniors by some ten years; we felt like social outcasts. We worked full days, with only the promise that, as soon as the busy season was over, we would get the study days due us.

For us, accustomed to city life—entertainment, comforts and ease—those were difficult weeks. I, with no more contact with my home, was hit the hardest.

I wept that night for all these things, until my pillow was wet and my eyes hot and swollen. I wished that morning would never come. I didn't have the strength to face another day of back-breaking toil in the exhausting heat. I couldn't bear it any longer.

Days, weeks and months passed in this fashion. The situation didn't improve; if anything, it became worse. We might have gotten used to it, had Amos remained with us—Amos, our father and mother, teacher and adviser, the bridge to the new world into which we had been tossed. But an important mission to Algeria took him away from us, and our group began to fall apart. Some of the others returned to Morocco, others were still debating what they should do. I wasn't ready to admit defeat. I blamed all sorts of circumstances, but would not surrender. I couldn't dream of leaving Israel. I decided that the cause of the trouble was the place; what I needed was to change it. As Amos used to say: "Change your place, and your luck will change."

I applied to a kibbutz on the seacoast which had a youth unit of my age. Here, among young Israelis, I'll be a real Israeli, too. I'll learn the language, live near the sea and get to know it well, before enlisting in a divers' unit.

"What's your name?"

"Taboul."

"Say it again."

"Taboul!"

"Hey gang, Taboul-Tembel's here!"

That was the reception I got at the new kibbutz; "Taboul-dunce" they called me. Today I realize that they were not bad, by nature. They were merry and mischievous *sabras*,* looking for some amusement—and they found it, in me. They found my name to be very entertaining: "Taboul-Tembel." It stuck like a leech.

I flew into a rage, but my voice was lost in their jeering. What could I do against them? Well, I have nothing against them, now. They just didn't know how to get used to an "immigrant" like me. I was really somewhat odd, different—and they found great fun in this fact. Perhaps I shouldn't have been so sensitive; a sense of humor would have helped me overcome this kind of reception. But I was a boy of sixteen and a half, very sensitive and lonely to the point of tears. I swallowed all the insults, which very quickly made me feel inferior. I became raging mad over any sign of an insult, and I replied with savage curses. But I still could not express myself well; my Hebrew was ridiculous. Finally, I saw that I could achieve nothing with my tongue, and I began replying with my fists—good, hard, merciless blows.

"He's a criminal," they called me. "A Moroccan dagger."

Every day grew more and more difficult. I was lonely,

* Hebrew for native-born Israelis

strange, disliked—a gangster. On the surface I seemed to have become used to it. I was considered a good worker, responsible, and physically very strong. I grew accustomed to the kibbutz way of life, and the food. But socially I was an outcast. I used to spend my free time on the beach, all by myself, gazing at the blue sea and dreaming of the day when I might enlist, at last. I would volunteer for diving and take part in breathtaking adventures. Then they would appreciate me; I'd be somebody. I thought of my dear ones at the other end of this sea—about my father, sisters, Rosa, even

Yaffa. I used to think a great deal about her during those lonely months.

Was it all worth it? I had brought misery to my father and had broken off my ties with my family. Why? For what? So that they should call me 'Taboul-Tembel'?

I wanted to work at sea. The kibbutz where I was living had acquired a few fishing boats which put out to sea to catch fish. I asked the work foreman to put me on a fishing boat. He didn't refuse me, exactly; he may have thought that a fishing boat was no place for a boy who had to attend classes every afternoon. My reputation as a tough, undisciplined fellow didn't help either, since the crew would be living together day and night. No one said this to me in so many words; they simply put me off from one week to the next, from one month to another, for many months.

One evening in early summer—I remember this as though it happened yesterday—I was sitting in the dining room, waiting for supper. In came Micky, the conceited "kingpin" of our bunch.

"I'm going on a fishing boat during the summer holiday," he announced. "I didn't even have to ask for it!" he gloated.

This shattered me completely. He didn't ask for it and got it, and here I'd been begging and pleading, and they turned me down. Why? I knew. They disliked me because I was a Moroccan.

In the morning I packed my few belongings and announced that I was leaving. Where to? Why? I didn't tell anyone. The counselors talked to me and tried to get me to change my mind. But I didn't. Yes, I liked them, but I wanted friends, pals—and I knew that, here, 'Taboul-Tembel' had no chance. I had to start all over again.

I made my way to the city. It had been hard in the kibbutz, with the loneliness and the hard work, but at least I had three meals a day and a roof over my head. Now I had to fight for this. I worked at anything I could find. I slept in the public parks; I often went hungry.

One autumn day, I sat in the park—my home—dirty, my clothes wrinkled out of all shape, and looked at the grey clouds coming up from the horizon. I knew that winter was coming, when a public park would not be too comfortable. A full year had passed since my arrival. I was completely desperate. Yes, I had to return. Now I would have to work toward one goal—to save enough money for my fare.

Two girls of my age, and pretty, walked by.

"Uri has enlisted," I heard one of them say. "He's young but they took him." I gazed at her. She had long blonde hair and a slim figure—just like the girl of my dreams.

I had a new idea. Why can't I enlist, too? I'll try my luck, for the last time. True, I was not yet eighteen, but they might take me, as they did that Uri the girl had mentioned. There I'll find new friends. Perhaps I'll be accepted into the frogmen's unit.

That afternoon, on my way to the recruiting office, I was in a bad depressed mood. The future looked dark— as dark as the black clouds hiding the blue skies on the horizon.

Three

"Your name, please?"

That was the question I dreaded, the one I wanted to put off as long as possible. But how does one enlist without a name? I took a deep breath and said: "Taboul· . . . Taboul Cohen."

I waited, with a pounding heart, for the smile of scorn. The girl soldier facing me lifted her eyes from the papers on the table. She gave me a sharp look, with no trace of a smile. "You may find it worthwhile to change your name to one in Hebrew," she said.

Of course! Why didn't I think of it before? I should change my name, right away, and begin my life in the

army with a brand-new name—and brand-new luck.

"Maybe now?" I asked her. "Right away!"

"What?" She didn't understand what I meant.

"Change my name," I said.

"Well, not just like that. There's a procedure—."

"I beg of you," I pleaded, "it's very important for me."

"O.K.," she replied. "Glad to do it."

I was really grateful for her wonderful suggestion, for her kind face. No one had shown me such a kind face for a long time.

"Well, what shall I put down?" she asked. "What name have you chosen?" I looked at her. She, too, had blonde hair, tied in a large bun, and a slim figure— just like the girl who passed me in the park and talked about Uri's enlistment.

"What do you think of 'Uri'?"

"Uri's a very nice name," she replied, and wrote it down. "I am glad to meet you, Uri. My name is Nitza." She rose from her chair behind the desk and gave me her hand. I clasped it warmly. "Thank you, thank you," I murmured.

I knew that she didn't understand why I was thanking her so much, and yet, if anyone did do me a favor in this country, it was Nitza, an unknown sergeant at the recruiting post. She, of course, had no idea of the wonderful thing she had done; she didn't know that she was the first Israeli girl who had extended her hand to me—without scorn or a crooked smile.

"Just one year in Israel?" she repeated. "Your Hebrew is very good."

"I knew a little back home," I replied. "I haven't

made much progress here."

"Don't worry; you will, in the army. That's the best school for newcomers ... Now," she said, going back to her business-like tone, "we have the name; how about the address."

"Put down 'no address'."

"Come, now," she said. "What does that mean, 'no address'? Everyone has an address."

But I really didn't. I no longer belonged to the kibbutz, and I belonged nowhere else, as yet. "That's it," I answered, "'no address'."

She did not question me any further, merely noted down in my service file: "Address—none." I suppose this was the strangest address ever noted down in a service file, but that's how it remained, black on white, for a long time.

My first days as a soldier passed quickly. I learned many things during those days—how to make a bed so that it would be straight, how to arrange my personal belongings. I learned how to eat out of the elongated plate of the soldiers' mess. I learned how to handle weapons, to crawl, jump, to march in drills: "Left, right! Left, right!"

I learned all this diligently—and many other things, too, not only things that were strictly military. I learned something else—and learned it well, having been taught by bitter experience: not to allow anyone to make fun of me. And I succeeded. I made no friends at that time, but neither was I interested in making friends. It was more important for me not to have any enemies, sneering and poking fun at me. And I succeeded.

I was Uri Cohen, and they behaved toward me exactly as they did toward Uzi Berkowitz, Moshe Mizrachi or Giora Gatt. I waited impatiently for my appointment with the Classifiying Officer, who was to decide where each of us would be sent and the occupation in which we would be engaged in the coming years. I knew exactly what I wanted. I didn't have to think about it a number of times or in any way struggle with it, as did other raw recruits—where it might be better, or what's the best thing to be.

On the appointed day I was in a state of great excitement. I polished my shoes till they sparkled. I spent an hour in front of the mirror adjusting my hat at the proper angle, buttoning my coat—everything, to make myself most presentable. The mirror was encouraging. I looked first-rate. The uniform fitted me perfectly and gave me the appearance of an adult.

An officer with the rank of Major was sitting at the table, studying my service file.

"Commander, sir!" I saluted tensely. He saluted briefly and motioned me to sit down. "I am requesting," I began right away, "to—to join a frogmen's unit."

The officer gave me a searching look. "A frogmen's unit?" he repeated. "Where did you hear about it?"

"I know. Every army has frogmen—doesn't it?"

"If you are that positive," he said, very seriously, "why do you ask?"

Suddenly I wasn't so sure. Perhaps the Israel Defense Forces didn't have such a unit. Perhaps this was like my other dreams. I had never considered the possibility that there just might not be such a unit in the Israel navy.

"Is there any other unit in which you might be interested?" he asked.

"No, just this," I shot back. "To be a diver. I want it very much."

"O.K., I've noted it down," he said. He made some notes.

I understood that the appointment was at an end, but I couldn't leave, just like that, not knowing where I stood.

"How about the divers' unit?" I asked. "Do I stand a chance?"

He gave me a long look. "If you ever want to become

a diver, here's the first rule you'll have to remember: you don't talk about such a unit. Some things are top secret."

"Does that mean that there is such a unit?" I exclaimed eagerly, like a drowning man grasping at a floating piece of wood, not sure if it will bear his weight.

"I didn't say that," he replied tersely.

The appointment was over. I went outside, very much confused. I didn't know at all whether there was a divers' unit or not, or if I had any chance of joining it. Neither could I tell what impression I had made on the Classifying Officer. I was confused and restless.

On the next day we sat around in groups and waited to be picked up by trucks, to be taken to our various destinations. I was in Group Number Six, out of fifteen such groups. Each group was being sent to a different place, to a different corps, for specific duties. I wondered if all those in my group had asked to join the divers' unit. I remembered the officer's warning about secrecy and I didn't ask. I waited patiently to see how things would work out. But it wasn't easy. Group Number Two, nearby, loudly sang paratroop songs. The fellows there knew exactly where they were going; they had all requested the paratroops. They were sitting together, a merry, solid group. They knew they were going to a paratroop camp, and since morning, they had been getting into the spirit of being together, night and day, for better or worse.

The fellows around me tried to find out what was common to all of us. I listened with open ears, but didn't join the conversation. The others shouted at the top of their voices: "What did you ask for?"

"Artillery!"

"I'm for armor!"

"Me, too!"

"I asked for Air Force."

"I'm for the navy."

I turned my head quickly towards the last speaker. I recognized him by sight. He was the outstanding trainee in our company. I didn't know his name; it was my habit, in those days, not to ask for names. But this time I couldn't contain myself.

"The navy?" I whispered.

"Yes, a special unit of the navy. I hope—"

"The frogmen's unit?" I broke in.

"Sh-h," he cautioned, then added, in a whisper, "Yes, and you?"

"I requested it, too."

"Well, we're in the same boat," he replied, smiling. "Your name is Uri, isn't it? 'Silent Uri'?"

"That's right—Uri," I replied, ignoring the "silent" part of it.

"My name's Assaf Ron, of Kibbutz Hadarim, in the Sharon Valley."

A kibbutz? Suddenly I felt depressed. Come on, I said to myself; so what? Just because he comes from a kibbutz doesn't mean that he has to laugh at you. I must get to know him better. Together it should be easier to get to that secret and desirable unit.

"My name's Uri Cohen, and I'm not silent," I said, attempting to smile. "Do you think there's any chance of our being accepted into that unit?" I whispered.

"Did they say anything definite?"

"Nothing definite. I put in my request, they noted it down and that was all."

"And you're sure there's such a unit in existence?"

"Of course," he said. "Some of our kibbutz fellows are in it."

I felt better. If there is such a unit, I'll get there, for sure! I guess Assaf read my mind. "We may have to be stubborn about it, all the way down the line. But they'll accept us, you'll see."

"I sure hope so," I thought to myself.

"But it won't be easy," Assaf cautioned. "First of all, the entrance tests are very tough, and if you don't pass, that's final. Even later, if you make a mistake or something, they give you the heave-ho without a second thought. That's what the fellows have been telling."

"The tough part doesn't scare me," I responded firmly. "That's what I want to be."

"You think all these fellows are going to that unit?" Assaf asked, looking at the trainees standing around. "It doesn't look like it, unless the navy has lowered its standards."

I looked him over. He was well-built, with a baby face and black, curly hair, which contrasted with his light eyes. To me he looked perfectly suited for a diver. What about me—and the others?

All about us, the others were still trying to guess what had brought us together in Group Six. There were about twenty of us, native-born and newcomers, tall and short, thin and fat, brunets, blonds, redheads, a motley group which one can find only in our army—

from all parts of the country, various lands, different schooling. What united all of us? Assaf finally suggested something to hang on to. Seven of the twenty had some contact with the sea, as graduates of naval academies, or amateur fishermen or seaside dwellers. This wasn't too solid a basis, but on that day, and with the uncertainty I was feeling, I was willing to stake my case on those slim facts, hoping and praying that we would finally be taken. The military trucks now came to take the trainees. With a mighty burst of song: "To the paratroopers—Kefak hey! Kefak hey! Kefak hey, hey, hey!", Group Two boarded its giant truck; the driver wore a red beret and a paratrooper's wings above his vest pocket. We joined in the singing, to bid them farewell.

One by one, the groups departed. Not everyone was satisfied. The fellow who wanted to be in the artillery rebelled when he learned that he was being taken to a course for section commanders. Another grumbled because he was being sent to the north, even though he had wanted to be in the south, near his home. All in all, there was plenty of tumult, noise, singing, complaints. We were still there, as the area slowly cleared. Finally, we of Group Six were the only ones still left, still sitting on the ground, waiting. It was noon before they came to take us.

We clambered aboard the truck and it got under way. All of us wanted to know where we were being taken.

"Nahal, the Work-and-Fight Youth Corps," someone said. "Anyway, not the artillery. They wear black berets."

"Don't be so sure."

"Then where to? What's the mystery?"

"Wait a while. Soon we'll know."

We finally arrived—not at a secret base of a divers' unit, but at a tent encampment, with a level drill field, many vehicles and the smell of gas and diesel fuel. This was the training base for military drivers. I was boiling mad: "I don't want to be a driver. What's all this about? I want to be a diver, not a driver!"

On the very same day Assaf and I applied for transfers. We filled out long white forms. Assaf helped me fill mine out.

We waited impatiently for an answer, which took its time in coming. In the meantime we began learning how to drive.

One afternoon, as we were in the midst of our studies, Assaf was suddenly summoned to the commander. When he returned, a few minutes later, he was all smiles.

"I got the transfer!" he cried, waving a long brown envelope. "This is it, Uri."

"What about me?" I cried, in pain.

"Right now only mine has come," he said. "I think that the kibbutz must have put in a good word for me. They said they would, and I guess it did the trick." Assaf was so happy that he didn't think of me, at first, just of himself.

I sat on my bed in the tent, watching him packing his belongings. Suddenly he became aware of my grief. He looked up at me. "I'm really sorry, Uri," he said, "but you'll probably get your approval in a day or two. If I got mine, it means that they're starting a new course, and they'll certainly need men."

"That's right," I agreed, but I really didn't feel that sure. I had no kibbutz to help me, no one to speak for me. Everything was lost. Even Assaf, my only friend, was leaving. When would I see him again?

"Come, don't take it so seriously," Assaf tried to cheer me up. "When I get there I'll put pressure on them. I'll leave no stone unturned for your sake. You'll see." This I did believe; Assaf would do everything he could. But what would he be able to do?

After lunch, I went with him to the gate and stood by the road. The winter afternoon was brilliantly clear. A military jeep drew up. "Get in, fellows," the driver urged.

"I am the only one going," Assaf said; the words cut right through me.

"So long, Uri," he waved to me.

I remained alone on the road, watched the jeep until it disappeared, then I slowly returned to the camp. On the way to my tent, I passed the office of the driving course commander. I decided, on the spur of the moment, to have a talk with him. The commander was a grey-haired man with a kindly face.

What was it he had told us at our first review? "If you have any problems, come to me. Here, I'm not only your commander, but also your father." Father. Right now, I wouldn't go to my own father—but to him, yes. He might be able to help me. I sat opposite him and began telling him my story. I could feel the tears welling up in my eyes, as I told him about my father's home, how I came to Israel and the troubles I had undergone.

I felt my eyes brimming, and I was ashamed. I couldn't lift my hand to dry them. What would the commander think? "He wants to be a he-man, a diver—and he's crying!" The tears were burning my eyes and in a moment they would be rolling down my cheeks.

The commander rose. "Excuse me, Uri," he said, "I think someone wants me in the other room. There's some water in the kettle; you look kind of thirsty." He smiled and left. I quickly dried my eyes and breathed deeply. The commander was a real man; he didn't want to embarrass me. I picked up the kettle and poured a glassful of water; I drank some and dipped my handkerchief into the rest to wash my flushed face. By the time the Commander returned I was well under control. "I want to be a diver," I finished my story.

"I understand that," he said, "but I have your personal file here, Uri. You're not doing too well in the course."

"Of course not," I retorted. "It doesn't interest me. I don't want to be a *driver*. I want to be a *diver!*"

"Fine," he agreed. "In the meantime you are here, and you have to learn driving. Failure in the course will not do you any good in *Zahal**. If you don't do well here, it means that you can't succeed elsewhere. And do you think that the divers' unit would want a failure?"

"It doesn't interest me," I persisted.

"This you can explain to me," he said, "but your file will simply say: 'Failed to pass the course'. What's more, a diver should know how to handle as many

* The Hebrew abbreviation for Israel Defense Forces.

vehicles as possible. If you get there with a driver's permit in your pocket, you'll be that much ahead."

We talked for a long time. The commander promised to recommend my transfer and even to help me get it.

I left in much better spirits, but I soon was back in the dumps. I missed Assaf very much. He was my only friend. I had no other acquaintances, and his departure left me lonelier than ever.

From the next day on, I went at my driving in earnest. I had to digest a lot of material which the others had learned while I was day-dreaming. But feeling, as I did, that the course would help me get into the divers' unit, I kept at it. When the course finally came to an end, I received a driver's permit, just like everyone else.

The course ended on Friday. With our permits, we received our quarterly furlough. I hadn't taken a vacation since the day I enlisted. I simply had nowhere to go. Today, I wasn't thinking of going anywhere, either. I listened to the other fellows eagerly discussing their furlough plans and the entertainment they would soon be enjoying.

I lay on my cot and listened to the voices outside. Slowly the camp emptied and a quiet sadness settled over the place. The sun was beginning to set in the west, leaving behind a grey gloominess. Suddenly I felt that I couldn't remain in this lonely place. I had to go away, too. But where? Well, wherever the first bus to come along would take me—to the city or a village, wherever there were people, girls in colorful dresses, lights, the sounds of life. I packed my things quickly and went out to the highway. It began raining, first in drops, then in a torrent. A bus stopped at the station. I took out my wallet and just as quickly put it back in my pocket. I wouldn't go by bus. I had barely enough money for a night's lodging and one meal. I tried to thumb a ride. Many cars flashed by without stopping, all of them hurrying to get home before the Sabbath. Perhaps they didn't want to give a lift to a wet soldier. At that moment I hated the whole world—and pitied myself.

Finally a large military truck pulled up.

"Hey, Uri!" I heard someone call from above.

"Assaf!" I could hardly believe it. But it *was* Assaf, grinning at me from ear to ear. I hated him, too, just then. A month had gone by since he left, and he hadn't helped me get into the unit; he hadn't even dropped me a card.

"Come on, get up here," the driver exclaimed. "We still have a long way to go."

I scrambled up, with Assaf's help. "Uri, how are you? How are things? Say, you're wet to the skin. What's happened? You look as though the world has fallen on your head."

"Not the world, just my own load of troubles. How are things?" I repeated. "Rotten as always."

He looked at me. "Say, you're not angry with me, are you? I tried to get you transferred, but it was no go."

"You could've dropped me a line—just a few words!"

"Write?" he laughed. "You sure picked somebody to write!"

He didn't understand me. And why should he? To him I was a tent companion, someone who also wanted to be a diver, someone like hundreds of others a soldier meets in the course of his army service. But to me he was an only friend—and he disappointed me.

"Where are you heading?" he asked, changing the subject.

"Anywhere. It's my quarterly furlough . . . "

"Say, how about coming with me, to my kibbutz?"

"Just like that? I don't know a soul there."

"You know me," he said simply.

I didn't feel like going to a kibbutz. In a city, you can get lost in a crowd. But in a kibbutz, everyone knows everyone else, like a big family. I was afraid that the feeling of loneliness would make it very difficult for me. I was also hurt because Assaf invited me almost as an afterthought; if we hadn't met, he wouldn't even have thought about me. I was certainly sensitive, then.

"Forget all that nonsense," Assaf chided. "Come along. Tonight the gang will figure out how to get you into the divers' unit."

That convinced me.

I agreed, but my spirits remained just as low. One can never tell what the future has in store. We arrived at the kibbutz on that dark and rainy night, and I had no idea that I was about to begin a new, wonderful period in my life.

Four

We were sitting in the kibbutz home of Assaf's parents. The kerosene stove filled the room with a pleasant warmth. I was wearing Assaf's clothes, after the warm shower I had taken—a pair of blue denims, a freshly-ironed white shirt and a gray turtle-neck sweater. The warmth I now felt was far more than the stove and the hot coffee. It was the atmosphere in this home, the simple love among the people there. I sat on the sofa, opposite Assaf's parents, Hannah and David. Assaf, himself, was stretched out on the soft woolen carpet. His younger brother and sister, Gil and Tali, were sprawled out, by his side, listening to every word he was saying. We chatted merrily, not overlooking the tasty cookies and the hot coffee.

I didn't feel at all like a stranger here, but as though I had always been among these people. They suddenly seemed to be old friends, even kinsmen. I always thought that I was withdrawn, unfriendly; the past year certainly made me feel that way. But not on this Friday.

The door opened. Assaf looked up and declared, "Ha, the beauty queen's here!"

I beheld a girl of about sixteen, full-bodied, with

light-colored eyes set in an attractive frame of black hair. I looked at her and felt a flush mounting to my cheeks.

"Come in, Dalit," said Assaf. "What are you afraid of?" She was looking at me and blushing in confusion.

"We have a guest. Come on in," Hannah said brightly.

Is she his girl friend? I wondered. That Assaf sure had things going for him all the way. She was pretty, really pretty—her figure was shapely, in a pair of black slacks and a knitted woolen turtle-neck blouse.

"Say hello to my sister, Uri—Dalit."

Sister? Of course! I should have seen it right away: the same thick dark hair, the same light eyes.

"Well," said David, rising, "I think meal time is here."

We walked to the kibbutz dining hall. The skies had cleared and a full moon was floating along in the cool night. Countless stars twinkled overhead, each winking a promise to me. I walked alongside Dalit and wanted to say something clever—or just something. But my bashful tongue just wouldn't wag!

The dining hall was like a beehive. We sat down at a table spread with a white cloth. The ceremony welcoming the Sabbath was brief—a reading from the week's selection from the Bible, then a song about the passing winter, and finally, old melodies and Hassidic tunes. Everyone sang, young and old, at all the tables. The meal was delicious and festive.

That Sabbath evening in the kibbutz dining hall, I learned something: the kibbutz can be a wonderful place. A large family, around two tables placed together, is quite different from six young fellows sitting down to eat. Dalit, opposite me, kept her eyes on her plate and didn't say a word during the entire meal. I did the same, but I also stole glances at her from beneath my lowered eyelids. This had quite a bit to do with the spirit of contentment I was feeling.

After supper I went with Assaf to visit his friends, the divers. "Danny, Eitan and Ami," Assaf introduced them to me. "Certified divers!"

I looked at them with great respect. They didn't look different from the others, but their being divers made all the difference.

"This is Uri. He's dying to be a diver. I told you about him," said Assaf.

They all set about trying to find some way to help me. "Nothing can be done now," remarked Ami. No one had said anything, but I had the feeling that Ami was the highest-ranking among them. "He's asked for a transfer and he's got to wait for an answer. There are no short cuts here. It has to be done through the regular channels."

"But suppose there's a block somewhere?" commented Assaf.

"My transfer took half a year," said Eitan, "before I finally got it."

My high spirits suddenly took a drop. I was tired and almost hopeless. When I went to bed, at midnight, I couldn't fall asleep. No one will help me if I don't help myself. I made up a plan and went over it in detail.

It wasn't much of a plan; in fact, it was rather silly. But at the moment I was sure that it was the only way. Tomorrow I'd talk about it to Assaf—tomorrow... tomorrow.

I fell asleep at last and floated right into dreamland: I was a diver and I was wearing my black tight-fitting rubber suit. Around me stood a flock of admiring girls, Dalit among them—Dalit of the light eyes and black hair.

Saturday was bright and spring-like. The three of us—Assaf, Dalit and I—went to pick wildflowers. Beauty was everywhere—green speckled with red, blue and gold flowers. The blue of the sky, stretching to the horizon, was the blue of an after-winter day, but I hardly paid any attention either to the sky or to Dalit. She was still silent and, with the blue ribbon in her long hair, she was even more beautiful than the day before. I was all wrapped up in my plans; I wanted to tell them to Assaf, but not with Dalit around. My feelings were mixed; I wanted Dalit to remain, and I wanted Dalit to leave us for a short while.

I got to tell my plan to Assaf only after lunch.

"You're planning to do *what?*" he asked in amazement.

"Exactly what you heard."

"Uri, you must have fallen on your head," Assaf said. "This is a secret unit, understand? If you do it, I'll be arrested — and so will you."

"Then you don't want to help me?"

"I can't."

"Fine. Don't tell me where your unit is. But what's to stop me from trailing you?"

"Listen," he said, "they won't let you inside, anyway."

"We'll see about that," I retorted. "I just can't go on like this—I can't! I want to be a diver—a diver! Do you understand?"

"You can't get in that way, that's all."

"I'll get in! I'll go to the commander. I'll tell him I've been dreaming of becoming a diver since I was five. He'll have to be as cold as a submarine to refuse me. They need divers, volunteers—."

"Sure, but that's not the way."

I didn't think it was, either, but there was no other way. I had until Tuesday to arrange for the transfer, get my uniform, then go back to the base, pick up my things and say good-bye to everybody.

Again I spent the evening with Assaf's family. Dalit was there, too. Once I thought I was in love with Yaffa; I now laughed at the thought, just as grownups laugh at some childish idea. I never felt this way in a girl's presence. I was upset, happy and confused—all at once, and I also wanted to be clever, brilliant, to make an impression on her. She was very shy, spoke little, just smiled. On that evening, it seemed to me that she, too, felt something toward me, but I didn't dare believe it. I didn't want to fool myself. Who was I compared with the kibbutz fellows? All of them were native-born Israelis, *sabras:* they talked a live, rippling Hebrew, danced and sang so freely! I was an outsider, a stranger. And yet, it was a wonderful Sabbath; at least the weather was.

I waited, with pounding heart, for the next day. I knew that my idea was very daring, dangerous, perhaps even senseless. But, I said to myself, if I would have done only what seemed to make good sense, without taking any risks, I wouldn't be here. I just had to do it—I simply had to!

On Sunday we rose before dawn. I found my army clothes next to my bed; dry, ironed, starched. I was very grateful to Hannah, Assaf's mother. Assaf and I dressed and went out into the darkness. A cold, pre-dawn wind was blowing. We climbed aboard the large kibbutz truck carrying farm products to the city.

"Remember, I can't take you with me," Assaf warned.

"I know, you don't know me at all," I answered grandly.

"That's how it'll be," said Assaf. I felt put out by

his answer. Why do the *sabras* go out of their way to be nasty?

Morning. The highway stretched along the coastal plain. We could see the water from afar.

"I'll ask to speak to the commander; what's wrong with that?" I said to myself, for the hundredth time. He's not God—just an officer. I have a right to know why I haven't gotten an answer from them.

We rode along in silence. I was busy with my scheme, and Assaf had his own thoughts. He might have been a bit angry; anyway, I didn't dare talk to him anymore. Suddenly he straightened up. "This is where I get off," tapping on the window of the driver's cab. The truck slowly came to a halt.

"This is it," said Assaf. "Shalom, Uri, I may be seeing you."

"Shalom," I replied. "You'll be seeing me, for sure."

Assaf didn't give me another glance. He jumped down from the truck and headed for the narrow road leading from the main highway to the fenced military camp, beyond which were several long buildings, and, farther on, the sea. I jumped down, keeping my eyes on Assaf's figure. He walked on quickly without looking back. The knapsack on his back and the dark blue navy uniform gave him a stalwart appearance. I really envied him, then. I wanted to be like him, just like him.

At the gate was a long narrow shed, painted black and white. I saw Assaf raise his hand in greeting to the sentry. Just *shalom* and no more. He seemed so sure of himself as he walked by—no question of his belonging there. That's what I should do—a bit of self-assurance, and no one will ask any questions. I'll walk inside and ask for the commander.

I quickened my step, came up to the barrier and waved my hand with the same familiarity that Assaf had done.

"And where do you think you're going?" asked the sentry.

"Inside, of course," I answered, cocksure of myself.

"Your papers," he said curtly, looking at me oddly. I handed him my papers nonchalantly, playing the game up to the hilt. I placed no great hopes in my papers; in fact, they were next to worthless, but still, I didn't give up. The soldier looked into my soldier's book, stamped with the quarterly furlough.

"Sorry, you can't come in," he said finally.

I caught sight of Assaf, standing in the doorway of one of the buildings. He was looking very hard at me, much annoyed by the whole thing.

"I must speak to the commander."

"You have an appointment with him?"

"Yes."

"Who made it?"

"I did!"

"Listen, fellow," said the sentry impatiently, "bid me a sound farewell and beat it, what do you say?"

"I must speak to him. Let me come in," I said, almost choking.

I was sure that the sentry would tell me again to get going, but to my surprise, he glanced toward the highway. "That's his car. Go talk to him. Maybe this is your day," he added.

"Thanks a lot," I murmured. The sentry gave me a queer stare. I must have looked to him like some kind of nut.

The military jeep came off the highway and turned into the side road leading to the camp. My heart was pounding. At the wheel was a broad-shouldered man, young-looking, despite the pointed black beard that adorned his face.

"That's the commander," the sentry nodded. "Go ahead. Talk to him."

The jeep drew near. The sentry quickly flipped up the barrier.

"Hi, Yossi," the bearded man grinned pleasantly. "How are things?"

"Fine," replied the sentry, now known to me as Yossi. "Waiting for the big day," he said. "When's that? I've been hanging around for two weeks, doing all sort of things. When will the exams be coming along?" He paused, then pointed to me. "Somebody wants to talk with you."

I felt like a fool. The words suddenly stuck in my throat, as though I had been stricken dumb.

"May I say something?" Suddenly Assaf was at my side. "I'll explain everything."

"What's going on here, today?" demanded the commander. "Come on, Assaf." He turned to me. "I'll see you afterwards."

The jeep moved on under the barrier and into the base area. Assaf jumped into the jeep, alongside the driver. "See you later," he waved to me. As he turned, he managed to give me a broad wink. "It'll be O.K.,

Uri," I seemed to read in his face.

"Headquarters are there, in the quonset hut," Yossi pointed. "Straight, then left."

"Thanks," I said again, cursing my suddenly-stilled tongue. How would I be able to convince the commander?

"You want to join the unit?" asked Yossi.

"Yes—how did you know?" I looked at him in surprise. "Is it written on my forehead?"

"We're in the same boat," sighed Yossi. "I've been waiting for the entrance exams for two weeks. In the meantime they've made me a sentry." He broke off. "Looks like Assaf is through. Go get a word in with the commander before he goes in for a dip and disappears."

"Thanks," I said for the third time and walked rapidly inside.

"Thumbs up!" said Yossi, suiting the action to the word. I was still to learn that the gesture meant: 'Frogmen! Down and Under!'

A line of frogmen went by, dressed in their body-tight, black rubber suits. I gazed at them with envy and admiration, as they headed, on the double, towards the water. I turned left and came to the hut with the arched roof.

"Come in," came a voice in reply to my hesitant knock. The commander was seated behind a square table in the narrow room.

"Commander, sir," I began, saluting stiffly, "I'm sorry . . . I came here . . . without . . . "

"That's all right," he smiled at me unexpectedly

through his black beard. "Assaf has told me about you. That's O.K. We need fellows like you."

"You mean I'll get the transfer?" My voice was choked with emotion.

"I didn't say that," he replied. "I said that we need volunteers. If you pass all the tests that we give to all our volunteers, you'll be in."

"Great!" I exclaimed. "Wonderful!"

"But I want to warn you," he went on. "The tests are very rough. We show no special favors and give no special treatment. You're either a hundred percent or you're out in the cold."

"I think I'll make it. I'm almost sure I will."

"Good, we shall see. Self-assurance is very important to a diver." He grinned, somewhat mockingly, I thought. "Exams begin tomorrow morning at eight. You're in luck. Some fellows have been waiting for weeks."

Five

The sun was well up in the sky. It was warm. I never imagined that a morning at winter's end could be so blazing hot. My face was seared from the sun, my lips cracked with thirst, my throat dry as cardboard, and the heavy knapsack almost wrenched my shoulders away. Onward! Onward! Onward! I kept walking, my eyes fixed on the back of the fellow ahead of me. I knew that I must not stop and block those behind me. Keep going! No complaints, no requests for water. I had to keep going, on and on! For how long? Where to?

This was the third day of the forced march. We went up hills, crossed gullies, climbed sharp crags and slid down steep slopes. A long, tough road. Onward! Keep going! Now we had to make it all the way back. The knapsack on my shoulders was awfully heavy. I was wearing new high shoes. I felt the blisters rising with every step. The pain was growing stronger. Keep going! On! On! So you want to be a diver, eh, Uri? Then show them you can take it. This was an endurance hike to test our physical fitness, our ability to take it, to overcome hunger and thirst, weariness, to get along with the other fellows under tough conditions.

How much can a person bear—thirst, a heavy load, pinching shoes, an endless road? Apparently a person can bear more suffering than he himself realizes. That's how it was in my case, especially since I knew that if I made it, I was in with the divers unit.

I kept my eyes on Uzi, in front of me. I hadn't known him previously, but I knew his name was Uzi. You couldn't overlook him. During the days on the base, he was our uncrowned leader. No one questioned his ability. He walked ahead of me, lightly, effortlessly. I gazed at his solid, muscular body, his straight and proud neck.

This was the last in the chain of tests we had to take during the week.

I had never been examined so closely, so thoroughly. Again and again they checked my lungs, examined my ears, my heart, my blood pressure. All these tests. I understood. A diver must be in top-notch form, perfect. Was the state of my health satisfactory? They didn't tell me, just noted everything down. Are you color blind? This, too, they wanted to know. What did that have to do with it? I didn't understand it, but I didn't ask. I had no one to ask. We were surrounded by very serious doctors in white and nurses, pretty but severe, as though we were guinea pigs.

"You don't have to be a swimming champ to be accepted," Uzi said. He himself swam very well, just as he did everything else. I could see how easily he answered the questions, how quickly he put together all the parts of the square in the psychotechnological test.

One thing was clear to me: I had to make good on this hike. On! On! Keep going! My breath was coming in gasps. My left side pained me as though it had been cut to ribbons. Black circles kept swirling in front of my eyes. My soles burned so in my new shoes that I couldn't hold back the tears. On! Keep going! We just climbed up a mountain, picking our way through boulders and thorns. Gritting my teeth, I knew that, as soon as we reached the crest, we would clamber down the slope, then up again, then down again. How long? But I must not think about it!

I heard Yossi's labored breathing behind me. No one had it easy here. Uzi is not a typical example; he is extraordinary. I must not think about how tough it is, about the next crest, the thirst. I must think about something else—something entirely different. What, for instance? My father? No. Those would be bothersome thoughts. Better think about Dalit. What does she think of me? After this long trip, we'll take a weekend rest. How I'll need it! I'll be able to see for myself if Dalit likes me. Can it really be? My heart pounded at the thought. "Dalit," I whispered. Assaf had invited me to the kibbutz, again. Should I go? But *where else* can I go? But does she really like me? Well, let's see: if Uzi should suddenly raise his left arm, that's a sign that she does. I kept my eyes fixed on Uzi, ahead of me, as though my entire future depended on it. Uzi kept going with a measured step, swinging his hands lightly. Suddenly he began singing cheerfully:

"How good it is to lie on your back in the morning!"

The fellows in line tried to join in, their voices hoarse with dryness:

"How good it is to run out of doors in the morning!"

What the devil, I knew of better things to do than scurry uphill and downhill at this hour of the morning.

"Forward! Forward! Forward! To papa and mama!"
Uzi's voice rose higher. Well, Dalit neither liked
nor disliked me. How silly! Who believes in such foolish-
ness! Suddenly Uzi raised his right hand to his mouth
and made like a trumpet: "Who's tired? Come on—
forward! Forward! To papa and mama!" Then I believed.
It was a good sign. True, his left hand wasn't the one
he raised, but it was a hand! What's the difference?
She likes me. I'll offer to be her boy friend, and I'll have
a girl friend, at last—Dalit. But what if she'll refuse?
Suppose she laughs at me? You and I, Uri? Come,
now! Then—I won't ever be able to go there, no, never!
I won't be able to face Assaf, once he learns of my failure.

These thoughts were not very encouraging, but
they did have their brighter side. They made me forget
the agony of the march, and I almost didn't think of
the thirst and the blisters.

Around noon, the truck came to pick us up. That
was a stroke of luck. Another hour, and I would have
dropped from exhaustion. The other fellows also looked
as if they were in no better condition. Even Uzi showed
signs of fatigue. It *was* a very tough march, a strict
limit on food and water, a heavy pack and dozens of
miles each day. Still, a person's will power is evidently
stronger than he himself realizes; even I, unaccustomed
to walking, to say nothing of water limitation and high
boots, managed to hold out to the end. Now it was
all over. The fateful week of tests was behind us. On
Sunday we should have the results.

I now had half a day Friday and all day Saturday,
an unbearably long day and a half. In the afternoon

I joined the fellows who were leaving, aboard a truck, for the weekend. I wanted to see Assaf and Dalit, in their Sharon Valley kibbutz. But I was wrung out with weariness and didn't join the merrymaking aboard the truck. The recruits were still fired up about the week of tests; the veterans who had undergone the same experience a month or two earlier, smiled knowingly. The fellows talked about the tests, compared notes, tried to guess the results.

I sat in a corner of the truck, silently thinking about the same things. Did I pass? I thought of Dalit and decided I wouldn't say anything to her, this Sabbath. Not yet; after all, she doesn't know me and I don't know her. I'll let time take its course. People always say that there's no such thing as love at first sight. Perhaps there really isn't. In that case, what's this feeling in my heart? Better wait for the results of the tests. Once I'm accepted into the unit, everything will be much simpler, easier. One doesn't reject a diver so readily. One can say: "No, what's the idea?" to Uri Cohen, who only recently was Taboul Cohen and "Taboul-Tembel" but not to a diver. Uri, the Diver, will be someone entirely different. But *will* I be a diver? Have I really passed all these tests and exams?

Well, as soon as Sunday arrives, I'll *know*!

Six

"Uri Cohen!"

"What? Who?"

I gave the instructor a dazed look. Why was my name first on the list? I was sure that Uzi . . .

"Yes, sir!" I stepped forward. One after another, the rest took their places beside me in the long row, all those who had been found fit for diving duty. Uri, Amos, Gadi, David and Yossi. Strange, I didn't think he'd make it. I knew some of the fellows by name; others I merely recognized. I did see that twenty fellows had passed, about half of those who had taken the tests.

Everything afterwards seemed like a dream—quick, strange as though I had already seen everything in a dream, yet still wanted to see what was going to happen. We ran along the stone pier. The buildings were weatherbeaten and rusty from the dampness. We filed into a room that looked like a lecture hall. The walls were covered with charts showing divers in their black rubber suits in various diving poses. There were also diagrams in various colors, which I guessed had something to do with underwater pressure. We seated our-

selves around long tables. In front of us stood the bearded officer with whom I had talked, only a week ago, near the base gate. Only a week had gone by since then—and yet it felt more like many light-years.

The commander addressed us very seriously. I was so tense that I had trouble catching the words; perhaps he was using technical terms which I simply didn't understand. I did my best to get their meaning. He spoke of the duties of the unit we were about to join, the secrecy, the commando tactics which the fighting diver must use—deep down, alone, far from his base, in enemy territory. He spoke about morale, which was so very important in this unit: all for one, one for all. What did he mean? I kept wondering, and again I seemed to be dreaming—suddenly, I am a diver! I pinched my arm under the table; all it got me was a red mark and a wondering glance from Amos. I was still dreaming. Amos looked at me as if I'd gone mad.

"Testing your endurance?" he grinned, mockingly. His grin was like a danger signal; I was accepted as a diver but I still hadn't gained the friendship of the others. I must not give them any opportunity to make fun of me!

"No, it's just that . . .," I murmured in confusion.

"Let's have attention," said the commander, looking straight at me. I wanted to say that Amos was at fault, not I, but I just lowered my eyes and kept quiet.

"You may have passed the entrance exams," said the commander gravely, keeping his eyes on me, "but that doesn't mean that you are here for good. We'll keep on testing you, and whoever fails will find himself on the way out tomorrow, next week or next year—the moment we decide he is not fit for us. Understood?"

I got the message, all right. I knew that I had to pay attention and not think about anything else. "The commando swoops in like a bat in the darkness, like a silently-cutting beam of light, or like a grenade in a thundering explosion," I heard the commander say.

Around noon we made our way to the storeroom. Divers' suits, powdered with blue talcum, hung from the walls, trousers, shirts, shoes, caps—all made of hard black rubber and having a peculiar, pungent smell.

"Undress, everyone," came the command.

I quietly stripped down to my underwear. The rubber shirt was cold and smooth to the touch. I sat down to put on the long pants, following instructions like a robot. I had thought once that I would jump sky-high with joy at this moment, but here I was, very cold and a bit dazed. Each instructor had a small group around him, as he explained how to fasten the safety belt, how to put on the rubber shoes and the long fins, how to pack the air tank on the back and tighten it to the body. The explanations were very detailed. Every item of the equipment had a reason and an explanation—why and what for, and how to use it to best advantage. I stood there, barefoot, dressed in my diver's suit. The shoes I was given were too small for me.

"Try mine," said Yossi, handing me his shoes. "I'm swimming in them."

Yossi was short, thin and looked like a young boy. I wondered why he had been picked. He looked like anything but a frogman.

"Thanks," I said; the shoes fitted me perfectly. We donned our caps, which enclosed our heads and ears and even our necks.

"In time you'll decide whether you need a diving cap or not," said Zvika, the instructor. "I dive without a cap. It bothers me. But it's everyone to his own liking."

Much of the day was spent in drills: dressing, affixing our breathing mechanism to our lips and breathing from the tanks attached to our backs. We were briefed on the dangers lurking for the diver. We learned the meaning of motions made under water. I had never known that there was so much to learn for safe diving:

problems of water pressure, depth dizziness, the various cramps which seize divers and how to avoid them. Zvika spoke Hebrew, but it all sounded like foreign terms in a different world. I was eager to get into the water, to feel it gliding by my body, to face danger and overcome it. But for the present, all I was getting was a description.

"When you surface, you must empty your lungs of the air in them," said Zvika. "Never let this escape from your brains, or you won't have any left."

The fellows grinned. But I didn't understand. "Why?" I asked.

"Because if you don't exhale, your lungs may burst. And if they do, you'll have trouble keeping anything in your brains," said Zvika, as the others laughed loudly.

"Not bad! Not bad, at all!" cried Uzi in his deep voice. I was offended. Well, that was another thing I'd have to remember, in addition to exhaling—to keep my mouth shut, to cut down on the talk. I waited impatiently for the moment when we would be in the water; at last, then, I'd show the others a thing or two. I was a good swimmer, and that, I figured, should serve as a good beginning.

We didn't get to dive until the next day. When dawn came, I had already been up for an hour. We jumped up, dressed, washed. Our setting-up exercises consisted of a dip in the water, which was ice-cold at that early hour. At Zvika's command we plunged off the pier, dressed only in our bathing trunks. My teeth chattered. I swam about briskly, and was surprised to find that Yossi overtook me with great ease. He was a better

swimmer than Uzi, much to my amazement.

After breakfast, all of us lined up in our diving suits, along the pier.

"We are now ready for diving," said Zvika, in a matter-of-fact tone. "We dive, as I've told you, in pairs. A diver never goes down by himself. Remember that. Here's the rope." He tossed the thin rope to me; it was about two yards long. I wound it, as we had been taught, in a loop around my left wrist.

"Who's your partner?" asked Zvika.

David had already taken a step toward Amos. I wanted very much to team up with Uzi; the first try was very important, and being with Uzi, I felt, would make it a success. Uzi, however, was already standing next to Ehud. Again, I was prepared to feel offended, but the thrilling prospect of diving made me forget everything else. My partner was Yossi. We were ready— masks on our faces and life belts across our chests.

"Remember," warned Zvika, "if anything at all should happen—if you don't feel well, or if you cut yourself—give a light tug at the belt. You must learn to do this automatically. The belt fills with air, and up you go. Let this be the last thing you do before you lose consciousness, so that at least your body will float up to the surface."

Darn! When will I be able to talk that way, so freely, about life and death? Zvika knew no fear; he took everything in his stride. I looked at his solid yet supple body in the black diver's suit; he looked to me like a superman hero in the movies that I had seen as a child.

We were all set, long black fins on our feet, the glass mask was over our faces.

"Down and under," he gestured. "Jump!"

One after another, we dived off the pier. This dive looked simple enough when Zvika demonstrated it, but none of us could do it as easily—not with the forty-five pound air tank on our backs, and our bodies burdened with diving equipment. The water was quite cold. I felt it come through the rubber suit and cool my hot body. In winter the sensation would probably be less pleasant. All of us surfaced.

"Rinse your masks," ordered Zvika.

We removed the glass masks, spat into them and then rinsed them in the sea water. The whole business looked to me at that moment like a religious rite which had to be performed exactly; so Zvika had told us, and that was how we did it.

"Check the knife and sheath above the ankle."

We checked by touch.

"Fasten breathing apparatus."

We obeyed perfectly. We were ready to follow our instructor through hell and high water, although he was older than us by no more than a year and a half.

"Empty life belts!"

Zvika raised his thumb in the agreed signal: Ready? Our thumbs went down. Ready! Dive! Down and under! I arched my body into the water. Dive down, down! The deep water was colder than the top layer. Now what? I wasn't going down! What the devil—I saw Uzi dive and disappear into the water, leaving a stream of bubbles in his wake. The rope on my wrist drew taut; my partner, Yossi, was down. I was floating—what was wrong with me?

"Nothing wrong," grinned Zvika. "We have to balance the weights above your thighs. You're too light. The rubber suit keeps you afloat."

"I'm light?" I retorted. "How about him?" I pointed to Yossi. "I'm much heavier than he is."

"His belt has more weights in it. I didn't put enough in yours. I took you to be much heavier than you are.

Here, try it now," he added, after the adjustment.

This time I made it. I forced my eyes open, fighting the first impulse to close them. But they were protected by the glass bubble. Not a single drop of water had seeped through. I could look ahead, wide-eyed. I drew a deep breath. The air, coming to me from the tank, was clean and pure. Inhaling was accompanied by a light whistling sound; exhaling brought on a sort of rattle of bubbles. Yossi was gliding alongside, hands drawn back, his body level, as we had been taught. The spot was none too deep. Below was white sand, soft and bright, covered with small green algae. Tiny fish flashed by and gave me a surprised stare. The bright sun penetrated the water, almost blinding me. I moved my fins and felt myself moving on. A slight tug at my wrist. My partner, Yossi, using the agreed signal, wanted to know how I was doing. I tugged at the rope: "Everything's fine! Wonderful! Great!" I don't know if Yossi got it all from the one tug, but I thought he grinned at me from behind the glass mask. At that moment I began to like him, to like the whole world!

Zvika approached underwater and looked me over, checking my movements, the mask on my face, the fins. I saw, or thought I saw, a look of approval on his face, inside the mask. I felt fine; everything was in order and would remain so. No more failure or disappointments.

The drills lasted from an early hour to darkness, day after day. They were really tough, demanding strength and stamina, a strong will and top physical form. I struggled with all the difficulties and overcame them. But not everyone did. At the end of the first week

David left; he gave up and was canceled out. Gadi had physical problems and was transferred to another unit. Now I knew what Yiftah, our commander, meant when he said that passing the tests didn't make one fit for the unit. Failure and transfer could come later—tomorrow, in a month, in a year. This, I knew, must never happen to me, under any conditions. I did everything that I had to, and more. I was the first to volunteer for every task, and tried to do it two hundred per cent well, not just one hundred.

At the same time, I was careful to stick to the rule I had made when I had entered the army: to be reserved with others, to withdraw into my own shell, not to get friendly with anyone, not to give people a chance to hurt me. But I also saw to it that nobody should take me for a softie. A command unit was no place for that kind. I didn't talk much, but if someone made a nasty remark about me, I let him have the back of my hand. I didn't overlook any slight or insult, and in this kind of argument I always tried to have the last say. Assaf, being more advanced than I, was in another unit; I really had no one I could call a friend.

Socially, I was not doing very well in the divers' unit, but this didn't bother me. As long as I did well in training and could show the group that I was a man, that was enough. This, at least, was what I used to say to myself. I took no part in social affairs. I remained in my room, reading the French magazine I bought, and kept thinking about Father, Rosa and the family. For my furloughs I went to Kibbutz Hadarim, then thought of Dalit, and loved her—from a distance.

Seven

Weeks and months passed since I had become a diver in a Zahal diving unit. My dream had come true. One morning, at the end of the summer, we were out in the open sea, practicing long-distance swimming, diving, and underwater approach to "enemy objectives."

Something long and dark suddenly came toward us, churning up the blue waters. "A torpedo boat," said Zvika, gazing at the approaching craft. "I wonder what's up." The boat drew near. A man in navy uniform beckoned, and Zvika swam over.

"Something's happened?" we wondered, watching Zvika as he talked with the man bending over the side of the boat. Zvika came back in a few minutes. "I need a volunteer," he said. "Which one of you fellows is ready for it?" His eyes passed over our heads. It seemed that each one of us tried to stand out and show that he was the one who should be chosen for the unknown task.

"I bet he'll take Uzi," I whispered to Yossi, at my side. Zvika's eyes came to rest on me, as if he had heard my remark.

"Come on, Uri," he called out. To the others he said,

"You fellows climb aboard the torpedo boat and return to the base."

"What's up?" growled Uzi. He wasn't the only disappointed one. The other divers looked at me in envy: why had I been selected? But they had their orders. They climbed briskly aboard, their black suits dripping.

"Good luck!" Yossi called. I really liked him—had liked him, in fact, from the day he helped me get to talk to the commander. He was a warm, decent fellow. I felt sorry for him. I didn't think he could hold out long. True, he was fine in training, but what about later? I couldn't see this thin youngster as a commando, and I already felt the pain that lay in store for him.

The torpedo boat was already some distance away. "What's up, Zvika?" I asked, all excited.

"Nothing world-shaking," he grinned. "One of our destroyers lost an anchor somewhere around here, and we have to find it."

"An anchor?" I repeated.

"You have to do such things, too, once in a while," remarked Zvika. "Two cutters will be here soon. Each of us will get into a cradle, behind the boats, and start looking."

I knew exactly what the cradles were and how we were going to handle the search. The two motor cutters came up very quickly. Each carried bright yellow "cradles"—cylindrical air tanks. I tied the round cradle to the rear of one boat and fastened it to the bottom, underneath. Zvika did the same with the other boat.

"Change the tanks," he said. "You can't tell how long it will take." Expertly I took the cylinders off my back and put on the others. This was so much a matter of routine that I did it automatically. All of the equipment items had long become part of me.

"Fit this around your helmet," Zvika said, handing me the black communications instrument. The earpieces were attached to a telephone wire, stretching from the boat to my ear. Inside the helmet was a very sensitive microphone, capable of picking up the slightest sound that I might make. I dropped down to the cradle attached to the bottom of the boat. The cradle was built like an oval raft with a glass-enclosed compartment in front. I stretched out full length in the cradle, with my head in the closed compartment and my eyes set on the glass pane. The noonday summer sun shone down and lit up the sea floor. Through my earpieces came taps—Zvika's signal that he was ready in his cradle. I did the same.

"Ready! We're about to move!" I heard the command given on the boat. A moment later I felt the light lurch of the cradle. I was carried along at high speed, as my eyes searched the rocks and sand for the metal object. The cradle was used for just such purposes; a diver would pass out if he had to swim such distances under water. Here no effort was called for on my part, merely to lie down and look. The boats went back and forth, as Zvika and I kept peering into the depths. Fish kept flashing by; some were interested enough to stop and look, others paid not the slightest attention to us. A codfish, always curious, gave me a long stare (Uzi called a cod "Aunt Bessy" because it had an annoying stare, just like his real Aunt Bessy).

I smiled to myself at the sight of this doltish-looking fish. It did look like a gossip-seeker. I wondered what Uzi's aunt would say if she knew about the fish that bore her name.

Suddenly I thought I saw something, a dark object that could be an anchor, resting on a sharp, brown boulder. Actually, it was more of a hillock than a boulder. Such rises, reaching more than fifteen feet above the sea floor, were common in the area, marked with clefts and valleys running among them. I rapped sharply three times, on the side of the cradle, as pre-arranged; the fine microphone under my helmet picked up the signal and transmitted it to the boat above, indicating that I had seen something and was going down.

The answer came at once: "Fine! We'll be waiting for you here. Good luck!"

I slipped off the cradle and began diving. This time I was alone. Generally, a diver doesn't go down without a partner. But this was not a battle action, just a matter of coming up with a lost anchor. And I really wanted to be the one to find it—I and no other. I was well-trained and felt no fear whatsoever. I had all the items necessary for diving: a depth gauge on my left hand and a compass on my right. A long, thin flashlight with a fixed lamp at one end was stuck in my belt. I would need the flashlight to see the anchor chain, if it had fallen into a crevice. I dived head first, my hands firm at my sides; the fins took me down. The curious cod-fish kept trailing me to see what all the excitement was about.

"Get the devil away from here, Aunt Bessy," I muttered, silently, of course, since you don't talk under-water, but I meant it. The codfish trailing me was a pest. True, the fish was harmless, but its silly stare was a nuisance. The fish showed no intention of leaving.

The flashlight was attached to a band around my wrist. I stretched my hand out and waved the flash-light at the cod—and it slipped from my fingers! It wobbled a bit in the water, then sank to the bottom. I dived down, down—forgetting all about the danger.

"See what you've done!" I snarled at the cod, as I dove quickly to retrieve the flashlight.

Suddenly I had a strange feeling. My eyes grew heavy and I longed for sleep. "Uri! Uri! Are you all right? Have you found anything?" I heard a voice coming through the earphones. "Rap twice near the micro-phone if you're all right."

My hands felt heavy. I couldn't lift them. The diz-ziness was terrible. Only this feeling kept me from fall-ing asleep. I was so tired, and so was the poor cod.

"Uri! Uri!" Again the metallic voice rang in my ears. Suddenly all the fatigue vanished. I was in won-derful spirits; I remembered the flashlight. There, below, at the bottom, were thousands of flashlights, inviting me to come down and get them. I moved about, eager to go down, down!

I didn't know that I was diving to my death, that I had been stricken with depth-drunkenness, which can be fatal to divers. I seemed to be standing at the threshold of some water paradise, full of evergreen forests, with branches of yellow, red and gold waving at me.

The cod which had been trailing me looked sick. Why should the poor thing suffer? "Listen, you poor fellow, it's hard for you to breathe, isn't it? Here, take my breathing tube. I don't need it. I can breathe without it. Hey, Aunt Bessy, didn't you know I can do anything?"

"Uri! Come up at once! It's an order!" Zvika's voice jarred my eardrums. Well, what's up? Why is he so excited? Anyway, an order is an order. I began rising and the strange sensation passed.

Now I knew what I had to do. At twenty feet I paused a bit, then rose and rested again at ten feet, to ease the pressure which a diver meets in great depths—otherwise, he might be stricken with convulsions and paralysis. I remembered these warnings very well.

When I finally climbed aboard the boat, I was greeted with a black scowl. "Uri, have you gone mad?" demanded Zvika. "Diving alone is absolutely forbidden. That's one rule you may not break."

"True, but . . ." I mumbled, trying to justify myself.

"And to go down that way!" Zvika cried, reminding me of what I already knew.

"So that's what the famous depth-drunkenness is like," I said.

"You could have passed out just like that," said Zvika. "We've had such cases. Gadi went down a year ago and didn't come up. Get it? He never came up. We didn't even recover his body."

Now I understood how close I had come to that point. Had I removed the breathing apparatus from my mouth, I would have choked quickly. A diver stricken with depth-intoxication has no control over his actions. He is first stricken with dizziness and fatigue, then this oppressive sensation passes. I had never had this feeling before. Never had I felt so self-assured, so strong and happy. I suddenly remembered that, in the depths, I heard my father's voice. He seemed so near, I wanted to touch him. Almost two years had passed since I'd last seen him. But this was just a mirage of depth-intoxication.

"Are you all right, now?" Zvi asked, giving me a worried look.

"Sure, but I'm as cold as ice."

The sun was down and I felt frozen. My wet suit made me shiver. The boat was on its way to the pier. As soon as it was moored, I hurried ashore.

"You won't tell about what I did today," I pleaded with my instructor. "Please, Zvika."

"Of course I'll have to report it—just as I have to report everything," he answered. I knew that this would be his answer, and I was afraid of it. Without ever having seen what was in my file, I was sure that all the technical reports about me were good, perhaps even more than that. My action today could do a lot of damage!

I ran all the way to my room. I knew that nothing hot that I drank would warm me, not a blanket, nor warm clothes. What I needed was a hot shower. I took my clothes, a towel and soap and hurried to the shower room. The thought of the stream of hot water on my body was very pleasant.

I never got there. "Uri!" I heard a voice behind me. It was Amos. "The commander said that you should see him as soon as you get back."

"Darn it." The shower would have to wait. But this didn't bother me as much as the commander's urgent summons. What could he want of me? Had Zvika already reported what happened? What was the rush? But it could be something else. He had ordered that I be called as soon as I came back, which meant that the order had been given *before* we returned, so that Zvika *couldn't* already have made his report. What could it be?

I hurried to the commander's room, still clad in my diving suit and shoes; I had taken off the helmet, the breathing apparatus and the air tanks. I rapped lightly on the door.

"Come in," came from the other side of the door.

"You want to see me, Yiftah?" I stood at the table. I hadn't been calling the bearded officer by the formal name of "commander" for some time. He was Yiftah to all of us. In our unit there was no room for official titles and formalities.

"Sit down, Uri," he said, soberly, without giving me much time to ponder. He went right to the subject, as he always did. "I think we'll have to transfer you out."

"What?" I cried. "You're discharging me from the unit?"

"I wouldn't put it that sharply. I'm simply transferring you to another unit, where I think you might fit in better."

"But why? What's wrong with me?" I knew that a transfer was no prize. Any transfer out was a sign of some failure.

"Don't you really know the reason?" he asked me in turn.

"Does it have anything to do with what happened today?"

"Did something happen?" he asked with a piercing glance. "What happened? Another quarrel?"

"No, no, something else. Zvika will report it to you."

"It's better that you should tell me."

"Later—first tell me why you are booting me out."

For a moment I forgot who was in charge. I regretted my mention of the day's incident; I didn't need more accusations. Yiftah's face told me that my personal file had enough reason, even if I didn't know what it was. My own feeling all along was that I was doing well. Could I really have been so mistaken?

"Don't I dive well? Are there any complaints about my work?" I asked, trying to be brave and tough.

"No, you're all right, as far as diving goes," replied Yiftah. I felt much relieved; at least I had not been fooling myself.

"Then why?"

"Don't you really know the reason?" he repeated, unbelieving.

"No, I really don't."

Yiftah went over the files on his table until he came to mine, marked with the name Uri Cohen. Address: none. I really should change this odd notation. For weeks, now, my address was Assaf's Kibbutz Hadarim; that was my home. But right now my mind wasn't on anything but the heavy charges against me hidden in this folder—heavy enough to send me packing.

Yiftah leafed through the papers.

"I see that you are an A-1 diver," he said. "Here we have no complaints. On the contrary, you're doing better than expected. You've scored four out of five points for mining a vessel in the open sea, five out of five points for snapping an underground cable. Long-distance swimming, excellent; diving without breathing apparatus—long stay under—good performance." Yiftah kept leafing through the reports and reciting the results more to himself than to me.

"What is it, then?" I interrupted. "What's wrong?"

"You don't fit into the unit, socially. I'm sorry, Uri, but it's a fact."

"Socially?" I repeated, hurt. "So, I don't fit in here, is that it? They're all milk-fed kids, from fine homes and nice villages, sons of army officers. And I'm a Moroccan knifer, is that it? Address—none. A Moroccan knifer is not the cream of the crop, right?"

"Don't be silly!" exclaimed Yiftah, "and don't start pitying yourself."

"Then, what do you have against me? Just tell me!"

"Plenty," said Yiftah, going back to the papers. "On the tenth of the month, fighting in the club. On the fifteenth, a loud quarrel. On the twenty-third, some argument with sharp language. Who started all these? Uri Cohen."

"What are you trying to prove?" I asked blankly.

"This report covers one month only, Uri," remarked Yiftah, "and there are such reports every month."

"O.K., so I'm hot-headed," I admitted. "When

I'm insulted, I hit back. Is that any reason for transferring me?"

"You don't get along with the others, and that's enough cause to transfer you out of this unit. I've warned you many times about it, haven't I, Uri?"

Sure, he had, but I never took it seriously. What if I didn't feel like joining the group gatherings—what's so terrible about that? I never thought so. But Yiftah seemed to look at it differently. He saw that I didn't understand, and went on to explain:

"The fellows don't trust you. You aren't friendly. You keep to yourself, you don't talk, you're anti-social."

"That's what life here has taught me," I said. "Keep to yourself, talk little, don't open your heart to anyone—and you won't get hurt or laughed at. If you're wearing armor, no one will get at you,"

"Anyone try to get at you?"

"No, I didn't give them a chance. If I did, they'd jump at me, just like that."

"You're wrong, Uri," said Yiftah.

"I'm not. If they don't know what I'm thinking about, they won't laugh at me. If I don't talk much, no one will make fun of my Hebrew."

"Uri," said Yiftah, rising, "your Hebrew's fine and I see nothing funny in your thoughts. As far as your accent goes, I think the French touch adds attractiveness to your speech."

"You really think so?"

"I'm sure."

"O.K., but you can't throw me out just because of this nonsense. Let them not like me. O.K., so they won't marry me. What has all this got to do with it?"

"It has a lot to do with it," replied Yiftah. "When a diver goes out on an assignment he has only his partner—his one and only friend, in the depths of the sea, far from the base, sometimes beyond the border, in enemy territory. There's no one you can depend on, at that moment, except your partner. He has to be to you what you are to him—father and mother, a commander, a home, life itself. A partner can save your life or abandon you. He can do everything for you, or only ninety-nine point nine percent when you're deep down. This tenth of one per cent can cost you your life. Do you understand, Uri?"

"Yes, I understand."

"I keep getting reports about you," said Yiftah. "Whenever we pair the fellows off for training, nobody wants you for a partner. We always have to force someone into it. No one wants to go out with you—right?"

"That's right, but that's because—."

"Don't give me that routine again," Yiftah broke in sharply. "They don't want to go out with you because they don't like you. What's more—they don't rely on you. You're anti-social, and nobody is willing to have for his partner a scowling, silent and quarrelsome character. You may have a heart of gold, but no one can see it under that layer of armor with which you have enclosed yourself. Do you get it, Uri?"

I understood. I realized that the things Yiftah mentioned were no less important than physical fitness, courage and diving know-how. For the first time since I got here, I understood it.

"I've finally decided, on the basis of these reports, that you don't fit in. Here," he pointed to a pile of white papers arranged on the table. I recognized them. The first day we sat in the lecture room, each of us was given a long sheet of paper and was asked to state our true opinion of our fellow-trainees—who was tops, second, third and who didn't fit into the unit. We were told that, despite whatever unpleasantness there might be in this, we were to be truthful. On that day, as I filled out the sheet, I didn't think that the opinion of others would find me to be unfit; now I knew.

But there was some hope; I saw it in the struggle which seemed to be taking place in the commander's mind.

"I will put you on a month's probation, Uri," he said finally, "a month in which to change your personality." He leafed through the papers again. "It won't be easy, but if this unit means as much to you as you say, it won't be impossible. What do you say?"

What could I say? My heart and throat filled to the point of choking. I nodded my head dumbly.

"Very well," said Yiftah. "It's up to you for the next thirty days." His eyes ran over my shivering figure. "And now I advise you to take a hot shower. That might start the thaw that will make you fit to remain with the unit."

Eight

Following our morning roll-call, the traditional dip and breakfast, we went on to our regular training. Now I realized exactly what Yiftah had meant. The fellows were standing in pairs, in their black suits, ready for the plunge into the deep. Yossi was with Amos, Ron with Haggai, Donny with Buki—they were the regular partners. I was alone, and I stood there waiting for the diver whom Zvika would assign to go with me. Zvika looked around; Uzi was at his side, without a partner. "You said you'd let me go out with you," Uzi said to Zvika. "How about today?"

"No, I'm not diving today," replied Zvika. "Besides, I need a partner for Uri. You'll be his partner today."

"Uri!" Uzi stared at me as though he had been assigned to pair off with the devil himself. I burned at the insult. But this time I didn't hurl at him, "Who needs you? Don't do me any favor!" After all, I had taken a decision to change. I swallowed the insult and gave him a forced smile: "Come on, Uzi!" and handed him one end of the rope that was tied around my wrist.

We practiced our regular dive off the pier, then climbed aboard the torpedo boat, in pairs. Zvika took his place in the prow.

"Our drill today," he said, "is to get into the port area and attach mines to the craft designated for each pair of divers." Zvika's words carried easily in the morning breeze. "You must see but remain unseen; listen but don't make a sound."

The boat plowed through the waves out to the open sea. We were quite a distance from the harbor. Since this was to be like the real thing, we had to begin at a faraway point. The broad expanse of the sea was blue from one end of the horizon to the other. Mount Carmel disappeared from view. We would soon be covering all this distance back under our own power.

"This is where we begin," announced Zvika.

Our operational unit numbered six men: Uzi and I, Yossi and Amos for the assignment, and Donny and Buki to man the rubber boat which we would be using and which was to wait for us out at sea for the pickup after the operation.

We inflated the craft. The folded black mass which had been lying on the floor of the PT-boat now became a hard, round rubber boat. We stepped into it, one after another.

Zvika gave us our final instructions. "Each unit is to report whether the target was really the one which it had to blow up. Be careful about the identification, the time, and the details of the instructions."

"O.K. all the way," called out Uzi.

"Immediately following the operation you are to cut the undersea communications cable, so that no help could be summoned."

"Yes, sir, commander!" said Uzi, with a wide grin.

As much as I disliked that fellow, I had to hand it to him. He gave you a certain kind of confidence; you felt it even though you were going out just for a practice drill. He was so strong, self-assured, capable. I was simply envious of him, that's all.

We headed the rubber boat toward the harbor. To an outsider, this part of the operation might seem to be a waste of time, but we had to carry out the task in the same manner that we would do it in war or on a commando operation. Zvika was with us in the rubber boat and again went over the details of the assignment. Usually this sort of action would be done under cover of darkness, but we were still drilling in daylight; otherwise the operation was to be exactly the same.

"Discovery by 'enemy forces' means that they take you prisoner," warned Zvika. "This means total failure of the operation plus zero points for the exercise. On the other hand, you can gain the maximum of five points. Discovery after attaching the mine will get you four; discovery before the attachment will get you three."

"We'll get five out of five," said Uzi, "Right, Uri?"

"Right it is," I grinned back.

"Fine. We'll be seeing you later," said Zvika. "That's that. This is where you leave us, so as not to draw any suspicion."

We did it as we had been taught—a back flip out of the boat. Our inflated safety belt kept us afloat easily. We headed for the harbor, on our backs to conserve strength, hands along our thighs and the fins flapping in strong, even strokes.

"Shalom!" called the fellows in the boat. "Don't keep us waiting too long."

We were carrying quite a load. Besides the diving equipment, we had with us the limpet mines which we were to attach to the target. These were duds, of course, but they were the same, in size, shape and weight, as the real thing.

As we neared the harbor, Yossi, who was in charge of the units, ordered the life belts to be deflated; in diving there is of course no need for air-filled belts. We pushed the air out of the compartments and made them fast to our chests. Now we were ready. Thus far, no one had apparently spotted us—neither the coastal cutters nor the lookout crews. We were to continue underwater, hoping for the five-out-of-five for the exercise. Yossi raised his thumb in the agreed upon signal: "Ready to dive?"

"Ready!" we signaled, thumbs down.

"Frogmen! Down and under!"

The last thing I did before going under was to give the fellows a "Good luck!" grin. They stared at me as though I had lost my mind or had fallen on my head. Well, I had almost come to that point. I was ready to try anything in order to remain a diver.

Uzi and I were now well below the surface. Yossi and Amos were off in another direction. All of us had to cover several hundred yards to the harbor, get into the area unobserved, reach the target and attach the mines.

"Five out of five!" Uzi raised both hands and spread his fingers apart. We were going for all five points—that was what his gesture meant. I had not the slightest doubt that, with Uzi there, we would. I watched him admiringly, as he advanced ahead of me in the water. His arm was bent at a 45-degree angle, and as he swam he kept watching the depth gauge and the compass on his wrist. Our target was stationed to the northeast. We proceeded noiselessly under water. We knew that special spotters had been posted on the decks and lookout points, eager to discover us and garner for themselves the highest number of points in this naval commando-spotting exercise. The contest for this limited number of points was really tough, for both sides.

Uzi was the senior member, the commander of our two-man unit. Swimming ahead, he charted the course by compass; we could not see what was doing on the surface, and we had to attune our senses to the sounds in the water and to all kinds of surface noises. We were very close to the mouth of the harbor. We dropped to a greater depth, using our depth gauges to know how far to drop. Five or six yards under water was enough to keep us out of sight.

We were now in the harbor area itself. Ships were at anchor all around. We glided along the floating dock. Here, somewhere, was the ship that we had to "sink." But where the devil was it? Anyone who has never been below the surface can't imagine all the stuff that's on the sea floor. All the "treasures" in the world are piled up there—twisted pipes, rusty metal, barrels, empty cans, hoops, sticks, old shoes and what not.

Uzi tugged lightly at the rope to attract my attention and pointed ahead. There was the ship—gigantic, casting a huge shadow on the water. We approached it noiselessly and attached the mine in line with and beneath the stack in the boiler room, exactly as we had been taught; this was a ship's weak spot. Once the boiler burst, the entire ship was doomed.

My heart was thumping so loudly that I was sure it could be heard by those above us, on the deck. They were on the lookout for us; the slightest of signs, a mere movement, a wave or any sound could betray us. I was so immersed in the operation that for the first time since I had my talk with Yiftah, I forgot all about my trial period and the threat of dismissal from the unit. My attention was riveted to the underwater part of the hulk above me and to getting the coveted five points.

As soon as the mine was fast to the bottom of the ship we moved away from the area. Uzi clasped his hands in a "victory" sign, and I returned the gesture. The five points were as good as ours, just like that. All we had to do now was to find the cable, cut it and return to the rubber boat, waiting for us out there in the open sea.

But where was that stupid cable? It was proving to be more difficult to locate than an ocean liner with its name emblazoned on the stern. Where could that cable be? We moved about among the pipes, barrels and the other underwater junk in the entire harbor, all the way to the fishermen's wharf.

Suddenly I felt a sharp tug at the rope. I recognized the signal; Uzi was in some kind of trouble. What could it be? There's no such thing as verbal communication beneath the surface. I hurried down after the taut rope, almost hoping secretly that I would find Uzi in real trouble from which I might extricate him and thus prove that I was dependable. But when I came near Uzi I could hardly keep from laughing; he really looked funny. His fins had become hopelessly enmeshed in a fish net, and the more he struggled the more entangled did he become. I reached down to my ankle, took the knife out of its sheath and began slashing away at the net. The fish caught there first stared at me in surprise; a moment later they were gone. As for the fisherman above us waiting to take in his catch—the poor fellow would never know who or what had cut up his net. Although we trained in the area, no one knew of our presence there.

We went on searching for the cable. It was already noon. The devil take it! This operation, which had begun so smoothly, was now bogged down, all because of a cable that wasn't there. We were also getting hungry. At the base the others would be having lunch, while here we were, still stuck in the depths. We were also holding up the fellows in the boat, and we could imagine what they were thinking. The long underwater search was wearing us down. What should we do? My own thought was to keep on looking; that was our assignment. But Uzi had different ideas. He raised his thumb up: "Let's surface."

I didn't agree with him, and shook my head to show it. We kept on searching. Where could that cable have disappeared? According to Zvika, the cable was painted yellow, which should have made it easily visible. But where was it?

Uzi appeared to be angry and upset—as much as I could tell from his motions and the look in his eyes, inside the mask. He drew near and crossed his hands on his chest; this was the agreed signal for "the air in my tanks is down."

I was amazed. How could that be? According to my estimate, we had enough air for at least another two hours. Perhaps some mechanism had gone bad. Uzi didn't look like someone suffering from the lack of air, but in his eyes there was a definite look of impatience.

He showed me two thumbs down: "I don't feel well."

"What's the matter?" I gestured.

He put his finger to his ear. Something there bothered him.

Without knowing why, I had the feeling that he was lying. Actually, I had no reason to doubt him, but his impatience was suspicious. Still, perhaps I was endangering him by staying under water. I wasn't going to look for trouble—not while I was trying to prove that I was a dependable friend.

"Let's get out of the harbor," I motioned. "Come on."

To my amazement, Uzi pulled at his safety belt. It inflated immediately, and in an instant he was on the surface; the rope took me up as well.

"Do you feel that bad?" I asked, as both of us took off our masks. I was really worried.

"Oh, this is better," he sighed, floating on his back atop the belt.

"Are you crazy?" I hissed. "Here, in an enemy harbor? They'll spot us for sure."

"Nonsense," he grinned. "We got the five points tucked away. Cutting the cable would have gotten us nothing extra. Who needs it?"

"What?" I still didn't get the whole thing.

"I'm getting fed up with this make-believe stuff," he remarked. "Let's get back to the boat." He began swimming northward, with strong strokes of his fins. We left the harbor area, swimming on our backs to the waiting rubber boat. I was confused. I just couldn't make any sense out of Uzi's behavior. But I did remember that I had to be very considerate and friendly, and I asked, with genuine concern: "How's your ear?"

"What ear?" he asked, grinning broadly and showing his beautiful white teeth.

"Your ear was hurting you back there in the water, wasn't it?"

"Who said so?"

"You did!"

"I? Did you hear it with your own ears?"

"That's what you signaled."

"Nonsense! You didn't read me right."

"I read you very well, Uzi. You first signaled that your air was giving out."

"You're dreaming."

We kept on swimming in silence. Dreaming? What had gotten hold of Uzi? Perhaps I was to blame; all of a sudden I wasn't familiar with underwater signals.

"Then why did you quit?" I asked. "Why didn't we keep on looking for the cable?"

"You gave the signal for it, thumbs up, didn't you? So we went up."

"But that was because you—." I really had no words.

Uzi laughed at my confusion. "Come on, don't take it so seriously," he grinned.

"How about explaining it to me," I demanded

"It's quite simple, fellow. We've a party tonight, something real big."

"A party? What does that have to do with the drill?"

"Well, I have to have some strength left, don't I? We're going to dance a bit, have a good time—."

"Then you deliberately lied," I interrupted.

Uzi appeared annoyed. "I told you—you're taking all this too seriously," he remarked. "All this make-believe stuff is coming out of my ears. Imagine, looking for some dirty yellow cable just to tickle it—come now!"

"But that's part of our training!"

"We've done it a million times. I could do it in my sleep. I don't need it. When I'll have to do it for real— well, that's different. But just to waste energy on it, heck, dancing is much better, I say."

At this point I couldn't say another word; I was stunned.

"We got our five out of five," Uzi went on. "Now we'll keep quiet and forget about the whole thing. Another scratch more or less won't be noticed."

We went on toward the boat. Not another word was said. Uzi's mind was probably on the party which he would be attending; mine was engaged with less glamorous thoughts. Uzi had lied—that much was clear. He weaseled out and pretended to be sick so that he could get out of finishing up the exercise. True, there was no way of checking up on it or ever finding anything out, unless we ourselves said something. Uzi would keep quiet and expect me to cover up for him. I wasn't going to turn informer. But should I really keep quiet? Perhaps I should tell Zvika why we didn't go through with the assignment? But that would be telling on a friend—and I was supposed to be friendly. This was my first day at it. Perhaps I should show that I was a good friend, by keeping my mouth shut.

The dark boat came into sight, rolling lightly on the waves. I knew that in another moment my decision would have to be made, to tell or to keep quiet. I was still undecided.

Dripping wet and breathing hard, we climbed into the rubber boat.

"You took a very long time," growled Yossi. "We're dying of hunger."

"Mission accomplished?" Zvika asked curtly.

"No," I replied. "We attached the mines but didn't get to the cable. Uzi didn't feel well, and we had to surface."

"What was the matter?" Zvika turned to Uzi.

"My ear," returned Uzi, without batting an eyelash.

"You must see the doctor," said Zvika. "Seems to me your ears have been bothering you a lot lately."

"You're right," Uzi agreed. "I'll see him the first chance I get."

"Liar! Liar!" I hissed to myself, but said no more. I didn't want to be an informer. What would the fellows say if I were to harm one of them, especially Uzi? How would they react? I wanted them to have a good opinion of me; my fate depended on it.

Nine

Friday. The base was buzzing with last-minute preparations for the Sabbath weekend leave. The instructors were drawing up their long weekly reports, which would later be put into our individual files. We, the trainees, put our rooms in order and dressed carefully; all we dreaded now was for the top sergeant to pick on someone and confine him to the base. It wasn't easy to set our room in perfect order, but we did our best. I packed a few things in my side-knapsack. My heart throbbed at the very thought of spending the Sabbath at Kibbutz Hadarim with Dalit.

I knew full well that I would lack the courage on this Sabbath, as on the others, to offer to be her boy friend. But this thought did not depress me. The knowledge that I would soon see her gave me great joy. I took my knapsack and made my way to the gate. Uzi and some of the others were walking ahead of me. Uzi was telling them about the out-of-this-world party awaiting him that evening.

"Have a good time," I said, passing him.

"And how!" he grinned back. "Leave it to me!"

We went out to the main highway to thumb a ride,

each in his own direction. I stood by the side of the road, arm upraised. I hadn't told anyone about what Uzi had done in the diving operation. And I really didn't know what to do. I thought about it all the way to Kibbutz Hadarim. Could I turn informer?

On the other hand, could I remain silent? I decided that if Assaf would come home I would have a talk with him about it, as well as about the month's trial that I'd been granted. But if Assaf weren't there, perhaps I'd tell it to Dalit. Then again, this might be the time to tell her about my feelings. But what if she would refuse me? I would then never be able to return to the Kibbutz. Hadarim was my one and only home in Israel. I was afraid that I might lose it.

I was still deep in debate with myself when I reached Hadarim. Assaf wasn't there. He was away on maneuvers in Eilat. I sat with his parents, drank coffee and had some cookies, trying to hide my inner thoughts.

Apparently I didn't succeed. "What happened to you, Uri?" Dalit asked later, as we were leaving the dining room. "You've been quiet all evening."

"You want to hear something?" I asked suddenly, before I realized what I was doing.

"Very much," replied Dalit. Her voice intimated that I could tell her everything. It was a pleasant summer evening. We walked along the path, and I told her about everything: the month's trial, Uzi, my doubts. We sat down on a bench in the glen and I went on talking. In the moonlight I could see her eyes clinging to my face attentively.

"Do you know what the trouble with you is?" asked

Dalit, when I finished.

"What?" I asked, eager to have her opinion about the whole thing.

"You simply have to be yourself. I know you very well. You have—many good qualities, very many. But to me, it seems you're always trying to be someone else and to hide your own thoughts and feelings. You must be yourself and do what *you* think is right. I don't know how to say it exactly, Uri, but you understand, don't you?"

"Yes, I do." I understood what she meant. "I'll begin being my real self right now. I'll tell you exactly how I feel. Would you like to hear it?"

"Yes." Her eyes had a look of expectancy in them— and I wasn't fooling myself.

"I'd like us to be close friends, Dalit . . . I have a deep feeling . . . Well, you know—."

"I was afraid you'd never get around to say it," Dalit smiled bashfully.

But I did say it—and it came out so easily. I put my palm into hers, and she squeezed it warmly.

"I thought that you would refuse me, make fun of me—."

"But why, Uri? I've been wanting to hear it for a long time."

It was a wonderful Sabbath eve, when Dalit and I spoke about our love for each other, a true and beautiful love.

Sabbath was glorious—to wake up in the morning and know that it wasn't a dream. It was real: Dalit was mine, to spend the Sabbath together, to recall all

sorts of amusing things, like when she said: "How you looked to me when I first saw you." All this was in the past, and the present was full of Dalit's smiles and warm glances, her black hair and blue eyes. But there was also the future: the unit, the month's trial period, Uzi.

"You must do what you think is right, be yourself," Dalit kept repeating.

I decided to tell Zvika why the assignment was not completed. He had to know and to note it down in our files, mine and Uzi's. He might pretend to become ill just when he would be called upon to put everything he had into carrying out a real operation. This time he had pretended to be sick for a silly reason. He might do it again when his own life, or a comrade's, would be in danger.

On Sunday, as soon as I got to the base, I went to Zvika's room and told him briefly all about the operation.

"O.K., I'll change the report," he replied rather curtly, I thought.

I wondered what his thoughts were. Had I done the right thing? Perhaps he would hold it against me. All I knew was that I had a heavy heart. In the dining room, I ran across Uzi, and I felt worse. He was in high spirits, as always, and told everyone within earshot about the out-of-this-world party he had attended, into the morning hours.

"Uzi," I said to him, quietly, "I told Zvika. I had to."

I saw him go pale. "Informer!" he hissed. "You'll be sorry for this! You'll pay for it!"

I wanted to answer him, but kept quiet. I had drawn the line at fighting and loud quarreling. "I just had to do it," I tried to explain. "I'm sorry, really."

I left him. I knew that he could make it very tough for me. He carried a lot of weight with the fellows, and he could turn all of them against me—just when I so wanted them to like me. I wasn't willing to gain their friendship in return for a silence which might have serious consequences. I wasn't willing to pay *that* price for it.

On the other hand, my conscience bothered me. Perhaps I really shouldn't have done it. Uzi might have had a moment of weakness; each of us might have one, at times. Perhaps I should have closed my eyes to it.

Then, on the same day, something happened which proved to me that Uzi wasn't the honorable fellow that he appeared to be on the surface.

We were aboard a destroyer, on a training cruise. I was on deck, just after lunch, watching the dolphins at play. There's something human about these fish—the sounds they make, the gestures. At that moment they were having a lot of fun, leaping in and out of the foam at the bow and calling joyously to each other. A mother dolphin was teaching her offspring how to swim; she would move away a short distance, then wait for the young dolphin to catch up with her. I could almost see in her eyes the light of satisfaction with the progress her offspring was making.

I don't know exactly when Uzi came near. When I felt his presence, it was too late to stop him. He was

aiming his harpoon gun and, before I could make a
move, the gleaming metal arrow shot out of the barrel.
The missile imbedded itself in the little dolphin; at
once the water around it began to redden.

"Bull's-eye!" cried Uzi in delight. "How do you
like that shooting? There's nothing like a dolphin for
a moving target."

A horrible scream came from the mother dolphin.

Two others joined her at the little one's body. They supported it on either side, and then all the dolphins disappeared into the deep, leaving the white foam speckled with flecks of red.

"You, you murderer!" I turned on Uzi. "Why did you do it? What did he do to you?"

"Shooting practice," replied Uzi blandly. Then his face darkened. "You keep away from me, softie!" he hissed and went away.

How I hated him, at that moment. Anyone capable of harming a little dolphin in the water—well, Uzi wasn't just a liar; he was far worse.

There was no more time to brood on the fate of the dolphin. Our drill was to dive down to a sunken vessel and practice retrieving documents and objects from the depths. My partner, this time, was Yossi, whom I liked more than any other member of our unit. With him I'd have no trouble, no pretending, no playing games.

The vessel was resting on the sea floor some twenty yards below the surface. It had been there for many months; by this time it was part of the scenery. Its hulk was encrusted with layers of algae, sea shells and thick growth. Immense schools of fish circled all around us, as we made our way to the deck. The silence was overpowering, and the water, inside the vessel, was extremely cold. We stepped cautiously along the sloping deck, careful not to slip and lose our footing. Everything was coated with a layer of slime, rust, algae and rot. The door of the engine room creaked as I opened it, and I shrank back from whatever was waiting for me on the other side, but I saw nothing worse than the gloom of a sunken, lifeless ship. Actually, this hulk which we were exploring didn't look anything like a ship. The long months under water had turned the former sailing craft into a silent, underwater scarecrow.

We began taking apart a section of the engine unit—a worthless, rusty part of one of the silent machines. This was the "important instrument" which we had to bring back from the sunken vessel. I used my knife to pry, cut and hack away. The thick layer of shells made it very difficult to get at the part. I was so engrossed in my work that I didn't feel anything—no pain, nothing. I wasn't aware that I'd been hurt; in fact, I felt no wound. But suddenly I noticed a red liquid mingling with the water around me. Black spots began dancing in front of my eyes. I felt an odd weakness and suddenly my neck felt incapable of holding my head up. What had happened? The red made me think of the dolphins and of Uzi. But what was this blood doing here?

I felt the urgent tug of the rope at my wrist. Yossi was at my side, pointing at my arm. I saw a gash in the black rubber suit, as if a knife had cut through. The blood was gushing through the opening, like a stream.

Yossi took hold of me. With a single stroke of his knife, he cut the rope and tied it tightly around my injured arm to stop the flow of blood. I felt his grasp as he pulled me up towards the ship on the surface of the sea. I wondered when and how I had been hurt. Could a fish have passed and gashed the suit? I remembered Zvika's saying that it was possible—and that a flow of blood under water was very dangerous.

Yossi knew that, too; I wondered how his thin body could have all that strength, and again I was glad that I had been paired with him. My head was growing heavier. I felt weak and dizzy, losing all that blood. Yossi now inflated my life belt and we shot up to the surface.

The destroyer, large and black, loomed some two hundred yards away from us. As we neared it, I suddenly saw the little dolphin—dead, floating on the water, surrounded by fish feeding greedily on its white flesh.

"I hate him! Such a depraved beast! How could he have done it?" I muttered.

"Don't talk; you're using up energy for nothing," I heard Yossi say. "We'll get there soon, Uri, right away!"

He didn't know what I was talking about, and neither did I. A moment later, everything went black.

I was in the hospital for three days—and very eager to get back to the unit. I had just one trial month and I didn't want to waste any of it lying in a hospital.

"They say you were very lucky," said Dalit. She and Assaf came to visit me.

"You lost a lot of blood," added Assaf. "They got you here just in the nick of time."

"Yossi got me here," I said. "That's Yossi for you."

I had plenty of time to think, in the hospital. Would the month's trial do the trick? Again and again my thoughts were on Uzi and the kind of welcome awaiting me in the unit ... on Yossi, to whom I owed my life.

It felt strange—knowing that you owed your life to someone. Now I understood what Yiftah meant when he said that, in the deep, one partner means everything to the other. Had Yossi not noticed the odd motions my head was making, he wouldn't have hurried over to see what was the matter, and then—I hated to think of it, about losing all my blood on the bottom of the sea, the way the little dolphin did. How horrible it must have been for the mother to look on helplessly as her baby was losing all his blood! I remembered her cries of anguish, and I hated Uzi, really *hated* him!

When I returned to the base, following a half-week's stay in the hospital, the fellows gave me a royal welcome. My arm was encased in a large, white bandage, which was matched by my pale face, but I was in good spirits. I felt that now I would have no difficulty in getting along with the other fellows. Yossi related, again and again, what a state I was in and how incoherent I was, as he was dragging me toward the destroyer. Incoherent? Well, I didn't want to tell him or to explain. What I had already done was enough to arouse Uzi's murderous anger. I didn't want to get involved with him unnecessarily—and I kept quiet. Uzi kept quiet as well; he merely acted coldly towards me and, in fact, ignored my existence. He didn't greet me or ask how I was— nothing. I tried to pay him no attention. I knew that I had to keep away from quarreling; just had to.

One evening the fellows came back from a drill. They had finished supper and were gathered in the clubroom, as usual. I could hear their laughter through the open window of my room. I didn't care for the clubroom and generally stayed away from it. I still remembered painful memories of the youth club of the seashore kibbutz. All the mischief and practical jokes took place in the club. When the fellows were alone, they would play silly jokes, make noise and generally create a tumult. I didn't care for this. Still, there were three weeks of the trial period left, and I had to do something.

I got out of bed and made my way to the buzzing clubroom. On the other side was the sea, dark and serene. The full moon, floating up in space, was reflected in the dark water as a million sparks. Everything was quiet. I so wanted to have Dalit with me at the moment, to gaze together with her at the sea and to take her to the club. The two of us there would make it easier. But I knew I had to do it alone. I stepped inside. A blinding yellow light came from the bulb in the ceiling. The place was full of cigarette smoke, noise and laughter.

"Hey, look who's here!" Uzi greeted me at the entrance. "I thought you were either above or beneath having a good time with the gang."

"Looks like you were wrong," I answered amiably. Uzi's look was unfriendly; actually it was full of hatred. I could see his mind working, trying to figure out how he could pay me back and make me look bad. He hadn't had a chance to do it before, while I was in the hospital. Now his prey was before him, and he was sharpening his fangs.

"This is what is known as a change in personality," he called out. "I hear that Uri got a blood-transfusion and that the good-hearted donor was Yamimy, the nut. Now you see the results."

A howl of laughter filled the room. Yamimy was a queer character who loafed around the harbor. No one knew his real name, and he seemed to have neither home nor family.

By trying hard, I managed to join in the laughter. "This proves, at least," I said airily, "that Yamimy has red blood in his veins, real blood. I used to think he had sea water."

The laughter rang out more loudly, and I knew that I was on the right track. But Uzi didn't laugh; he was busy thinking up a retort that would hurt me. Finally he seemed to have hit on something.

"And did they give you a good dose of vaseline in the hospital?" he asked.

"Vaseline?" I was as surprised as the others. "No. They didn't say that my arm would need any treatment— no vaseline, no—."

"Who's talking about your arm?" Uzi broke in. "I mean vaseline for your tongue."

"If you're so smart, suppose you explain yourself," I said, "so all of us can laugh."

"You really don't get it?"

"No, I don't."

"You lick around Zvika so much that I thought you might need vaseline to keep your tongue well-greased."

A silence fell on the room. All the fellows now knew that Uzi was trying to provoke me, but only I knew the reason for it.

"A flatterer?" asked Buki, raising his eyes from the chessboard. "I think the trouble with Uri is that he isn't one. He doesn't flatter and he doesn't smile."

"But he's an informer!" said Uzi.

"An informer?" Everyone crowded around. Every face was drawn with curiosity. "What happened? What did he do?"

"With Uzi's permission, I'll tell you," I said. "You ready, Uzi?"

Uzi didn't like the idea, but he had no retreat. "What do I care!" he blurted out.

I told the story, in full. I didn't hold back a thing. Once I had decided to talk, I no longer felt closed up inside. Everyone's eyes were upon me. They listened intently—and suddenly I sensed that they all had something to say.

"You promised me, when you pulled off that stunt, that you wouldn't do it again!" Amos burst out, red-faced. "You—."

"Shut up," growled Uzi, turning to go.

But Amos didn't shut up. "I covered up for you, Uzi! I didn't report it or talk about it. Now I see that it's a system. Trouble with an ear, is it?"

"That's it," recalled Yossi. "Now I get it. You couldn't have gotten to the dock and back that quickly. You lied to me. You said you got to the target. You weren't even there, right? Admit it!"

Uzi paused silently at the door. His face had gone chalk-white and his lips trembled. He stared at us for an instant, then walked out of the club. An uneasy silence filled the room. "That lousy character!" hissed Buki. "This means that he's been endangering all of us for months and we even helped him do it. We covered up for him and his little lies."

I wasn't happy about it at all. Again I felt depressed. I was still weak from the loss of blood, and here in the club, it was terribly stuffy. I stepped toward the door; all I wanted was to lie down and fall asleep and not to think any more about Uzi and the whole messy episode. Behind me I could hear the upset voices of the fellows, as they recalled one or another of Uzi's lies. In one instant, the king of the unit had lost his crown and sceptre. How easy it is to rise and fall, I said to myself.

"Uri!" I heard a voice behind me. It was Amos. "Uri, you're a real guy, one hundred per cent!"

And he gave me a hearty slap on the back.

Ten

We went down to Eilat. There's no better spot for diving:
a smooth and serene sea, with matchless underwater
wonders, beautiful coral, enchanting fish found only
in Eilat, so marvelously fashioned and colorful that
one would imagine them to be a work of art, rather
than living creatures.

We were in Eilat two weeks without leave to go north.
I longed for Dalit. At times it seemed to me that Sabbath
evening was just so much lovesick imagination. The
last time I had seen her was at the hospital, but we had
no real chance of being alone there. I wanted to write
to her but didn't dare. Instead, I wrote to the entire
family and sent my regards. With my spelling and handwriting, I didn't have the nerve to write a real letter;
besides, I was still a bit shy. All I could do was hope
that she was still thinking of me, as I was of her.

My month's probation was up this week. Had I made
it? I still couldn't tell. Friendship and attitudes are
not things which can be measured by regular standards.
It seemed to me that the fellows were friendlier, but
I couldn't tell for sure. I did feel that I had won some
respect that night at the club. But respect isn't every-

thing. I had to convince them that I could be a true friend, someone whom they could trust in the deep. But how could that be done? Such things don't change overnight. The fellows had always behaved decently towards me, and I couldn't tell whether the ice had been broken or not.

I did know that now I had a sworn enemy—Uzi. There was no such thing as a secret in our unit, and everyone knew that he, too, was put on probation for a month. If he would be caught in a lie, during this month, he'd be out of the unit. "And if that happens," Uzi threatened me, "don't envy yourself. You're liable to find yourself, one day, in a dark street with your head inside a sack."

I was sure that Uzi was capable of carrying out his threat. I didn't want to see him dismissed, but not because of his threat. I knew what it meant to be dismissed from the unit, and I really hoped that he would be able to overcome the sickly tendency in his blood, to lie. He was an excellent diver, and his loss would be regrettable. But it was clear that the unit could not afford to have a liar in its midst.

I avoided him as much as possible—not because I was afraid but because I thought it would be best. I wouldn't open his wounds and he wouldn't push me into a quarrel which I didn't want.

One afternoon I took advantage of the free time and went out for some underwater fishing. The short breathing spells we got in Eilat weren't long enough to travel to "the North," but we used them for resting or for underwater fishing, which made up somewhat for our longing.

The Gulf of Eilat is an enchanted world: the multi-colored reefs, the fish, the tunnels and crevices. I was dressed in a diving suit with full equipment and a gun for underwater fishing. There's an army rule which forbids diving by oneself, but I was on vacation. For once I wanted to be alone among all this beauty. I glided along easily, amazed for the umpteenth time at this glorious beauty under the water. In the unique illumination of the deep, everything seemed to be the handiwork of some talented fairy—enchanted castles, ancient forests of stone, breath-taking fish of all sizes. I wanted to catch something, but it would have been a shame to mar this beauty. Why kill a creature and bring it to the surface?

A deep black cavern opened before me. Such caverns always attracted me; I wanted to see what mysteries awaited me inside. The pencil flashlight was hanging from my wrist. I switched it on and entered the black recess. A school of frightened fish flashed into the open. "That gave them a good scare!" I smiled to myself. And suddenly I got a good scare myself.

A giant flat-bodied creature came out of the cavern—straight at me. I withdrew quickly in fright. I recognized the creature—a hideous sea-cat with long, thin wings, flat body and a long, sharp tail. It came flying, irritated, its long tail swishing from side to side. I ducked just in time to avoid the tail's barbed and poisonous ridges. Luckily, it appeared that the creature was no less frightened than I was. Flapping its wings, it turned and disappeared. I don't why it is, but in the water you can find, side by side with the beautiful and delicate fish, all kinds of ugly creatures which were created for some unknown reason—the octopus, the sea serpents and other monsters which may not be very dangerous but whose appearance causes a person's hair to stand on end: wide-open mouths, sharp teeth, an awesome look. I didn't care to meet up with these. I decided not to probe inside the cavern; who knew what devils might be lurking there, in the darkness?

A beautiful large fish passed by—red and gold and silver and a deep blue. I decided to catch it and take

it to Dalit, as a gift. I cocked my gun. The spring was released and the arrow at the end of the barrel shot forth. The barb pierced the fish, sending it into a convulsion, and I drew it close by the string attached to the arrow. This would make a nice gift. I would dry the skin and stuff it.

"Actually," I thought, "my fishing was no more justified than Uzi's." I was suddenly sorry for the death of the beautiful fish.

Something above me drew my attention. It's hard to explain, but in the course of time, a diver develops a special sense of danger. Soundlessly a message comes to him, like a silent wave: "Beware! Danger! Be ready!"

I looked up and my heart froze. I saw the black, threatening shape feared by all divers—a shark! It kept circling like a beast of prey around its victim, moving in wide circles. On the surface, trapped in the circle, was Uzi. I didn't think twice. True, I was no hero, but there was no choice. There was Uzi, with the shark keeping its cruel eyes on him. What could I do? I was sorry that I had not put on my complete diving suit, with the knife in its sheath at the ankle. But then, what good would a knife do against such a gigantic fish? It was at least ten feet long. Its mouth ran in a thin line across its head. It approached Uzi, narrowing the circles.

I tried to remember what was to be done to chase a shark away. There are many different theories. Some say you should float motionlessly; others say you should flap around noisily, emit air bubbles from the tank, yell loudly. I decided to take action and raised myself above the water.

"Give him a squirt of air bubbles!" I yelled to Uzi. He did this with stiff fingers, but the shark was not impressed. I came nearer. "Let's yell!" I shouted. "Help! Help! Shark! Shark!" we yelled until we were hoarse. The shark kept staring at us, unmoved. He was sure that very soon he would be enjoying his meal. We waved toward the beach, but it was too far away. I remembered that sharks eat fish floating on the surface. In that case, we should dive. I fitted my mask on tight, as did Uzi, and we went under—and so did the shark. No, this was no good, I decided. The shark seemed even more at home in the deep. Up again we went; I had the feeling that, at any moment, the shark would bite off a leg or even two.

Suddenly an idea hit me. Directly below was the beautiful fish, with the arrow sticking in it. I had abandoned the gun and the fish when I caught sight of the shark.

"Get his attention!" I called to Uzi and dove down. Could he do it? Perhaps the shark would come after me, and Uzi would take the opportunity to get away and leave me. But no—he couldn't possibly hate me that much. I picked up the bloody fish, and as I did so, I felt the air contracting in my mouth. I knew the sign— air tanks were becoming empty, except for the emergency portion—enough for a few minutes. After that, I could do nothing but free diving—and be helpless against the monster shark.

I surfaced to find the shark still circling Uzi. We had been taught that sharks attack quickly, but this one was either too lazy or had not heard about the way he was supposed to act.

I decided to free the arrow stuck in the body of the fish and to fire it at the shark's head, though I knew that the thickness of that ugly head would probably prevent any serious injury. Still, I withdrew the arrow and fitted it into the muzzle. Just at that moment the shark, which was supposedly very near-sighted, noticed the bloody fish I had cast away and streaked toward it. One bite left just another chunk.

"Hurry, Uzi! Let's get out of here!" I called. We thrust forward, strongly pumping our fins. Only minutes later did we dare to look back. The shark had forgotten all about us. He was now busy with the rest of the fish, which was obviously much to his liking. We reached the beach, trembling like leaves.

"Thanks," said Uzi and went off, without another word. I lay sprawled out in the sand, almost in a state of shock. Where did Uzi get the strengh to walk away upright? I don't know. He was simply a tough physical specimen.

I don't know who it was that spread the story of the shark among the fellows. I didn't mention it to anyone; I wasn't eager to have it known that I had gone out diving alone. Obviously, Uzi wasn't likely to have said anything about my having saved his life, not for all the money in the world. This would have gone against his grain. I wondered how he even managed to thank me. But the story spread throughout Eilat. At our base the story was blown up beyond recognition. The lone shark grew into a school of blue sharks. The gun, which I hadn't used, was credited in the story with five kills.

I turned out to be an old hand at shark-catching. I became the hero of the day. A fisherman brought in the remnants of the once-beautiful red fish, gold, silver and deep blue out of which deep, round bites had been taken, as though a sharp knife had cut into it. That was all that was left of my fish after the shark got through with it. I shuddered to think that it could have been us instead.

Uzi took no part in the excitement. He kept to himself and hated me more than ever. I understood him well. The fact that I had saved his life had made it even more complicated for him, as a member of the unit. He could no longer feel comfortable in our midst.

At the end of that week I was notified that my probation period was over. "It's O.K.," said Zvika. "Yiftah said to tell you that you may stay."

"How about Uzi?" I wanted to know.

"He asked for a transfer," replied Zvika. "He himself came around to the idea that he didn't fit into the unit. I always knew the fellow was smart."

When we finally got up north, after a long period of basic training in Eilat, I was surprised to find that we were in the middle of a new winter. In Eilat the end of summer and the arrival of winter were barely marked. No rains came and the weather remained very pleasant. But in the coastal cities the winds blew hard, heavy rains drenched the area, and people walked around bundled up in heavy overcoats.

"We haven't had such a winter for years," they complained. This was a different winter for me, as well. I wasn't at all aware of the cold, the wind and the ceaseless rains.

"Cold?" I smiled. "I'm warm—real warm."

"That's the heat you saved up in Eilat," joked Yossi. "Too bad I didn't think of it while we were still down there."

This wasn't the reason, of course. The warmth I felt came from the heart, mine and Dalit's, and it made me feel good all winter long. It was the warm atmosphere I felt in Kibbutz Hadarim and in my own home— the divers' unit. I was no longer homeless. I now had two homes, and they made up for my having left my father's home and my family in Morocco. I was sure that this severance was final, and it grieved me. The small square room in the hut of the unit, which I shared with Yossi, Buki and Amos, replaced what I had enjoyed there. We covered the walls with photos of pin-up girls which we cut out of foreign magazines. The room was always untidy—definitely a room of males— ashtrays overflowing with cigarette butts and professional literature dealing with diving and the sea. I loved this disorder, the window opposite my bed and the view out to sea, the long talks we had in analyzing the "battles" and comparing "operations." I held dear all the souvenirs in the room—the finds we came up with, the colorful stuffed fish, shells and other trinkets, good luck charms and all the stuff which a stranger would regard as just so much junk cluttering up the walls and hanging from the ceiling. We wouldn't have given them up for all the tea in China.

At first we used to talk about Uzi. His absence was felt keenly, in the unit. We repeatedly took his character apart, probing, searching. I kept thinking about him, with a pang of conscience at times. Did he still hate me so much, I wondered?

But we didn't have too much time for speculation. We were busy training, many hours each day. The exercises were quite different from the summer drills. We now went out on diving drills in rough seas—something not too easy or pleasant. With chattering teeth, we donned our black rubber suits over long woolen underwear which was supposed to help the diver retain his body heat, but we were still very cold. We shivered as we looked into the purplish-green water, then dived in—down and under. It felt odd, plunging into the deep, with the stormy waves above and the rain beating down. The water was ice-cold, really freezing; our bodies felt stiff, and the cold hampered our movements. But a diver must be trained to go out under the worst of conditions. We went out in daylight and at night, in wind and rain, in thunderstorms and heavily-overcast nights, without a star shining, diving into the inky-black water with not a single human soul near us; silence, except for the huge waves and the flapping of our fins— our only motors which enabled us to cut through the black water and move ahead, quietly, quickly.

It was a tiring winter of constant drilling, a cold, wet winter. But for me it was the happiest winter of my life. Nothing deterred me and no assignment was too difficult. I had found my place, my home, and I loved Dalit with all my heart.

Eleven

I could go on with the story endlessly. So many things happened during those years—long drills, hair-raising underwater adventures, toughening of body and spirit, the miles of words and the tons of glances exchanged with Dalit. How can one tell every small detail? Let me therefore try to give only the highlights, the turning points in my life.

I completed the diving course with the rank of master-sergeant and certified diver, and became an instructor, replacing Zvika, following his discharge. One by one, all my friends left the unit and returned to civilian life. Assaf went back to Kibbutz Hadarim, Yossi and Buki enrolled in Hebrew University, Amos entered the Technion. Despite our having gone our separate ways, we kept in touch with each other. We met on reserve duty and at other times.

I now had many new friends and was finding it easy to make more. I was now serving in the unit on a regular basis. Since the difficulties I had in getting settled were now behind me, my life was like a story book. Only a few years ago I was homeless, and here I had two homes—the naval base and Hadarim. But I wasn't content; I wanted a third home—Dalit's and mine. We decided to be married and build our own home in the kibbutz.

I was really happy then; I had everything going for me. If only Father would have answered my letters, or if my sisters would have shown some sign of life! But I guess nobody can have everything, and I did have my share and more. I sent my father a letter to tell him about my approaching marriage. I told him how I was getting along and asked him if he thought I should remain in regular military service or go back to the kibbutz and work in the barn, the garage or the vineyard. I begged him to answer me, to come to my wedding. But he didn't write back; he kept silent. Only good-hearted Rosa sent me a message of congratulations.

My marriage to Dalit took place on the large kibbutz lawn. The summer night was soft and fragrant. All my friends from the navy and the kibbutz were there. Dalit, dressed in white, stood at my side. She was so beautiful that I caught my breath every time I looked at her.

Our honeymoon (we had only one week) was spent in travel. I took Dalit to all the places where I had trained; I even got her to put on a diving suit and plunge into the water. She was reluctant at first but once she did, she took a liking to it. She showed a real talent for diving, and was really excited by the wonders of the deep. "Gosh, Uri! I never imagined it to be so beautiful!" she exclaimed when she came up, all dripping. "Now I know why you love diving so much."

"That's right," I smiled. "But diving is more than

that, Dalit. It means danger and long periods away from home."

"I know," she replied seriously. "And I know that you feel that your place is here." She understood me and urged me to stay in the regular service. I saw the military as a career, and serving in it gave me the confidence that made my life complete.

I was sent to an officers' training school. It was a long, tough course. During that period I came home at rare intervals. But Dalit never complained about our long separations. She understood.

When our first son was born, my happiness knew no bounds. I so wanted a son! I wanted him to be everything I was hoping for. I promised myself to be an understanding father, never to strike my son or force my will upon him. We called him "Gal," which means a wave.

I cabled my father about the birth of his grandson, just as a matter of form. I had no more hope of hearing from him this time than I had previously. But life is full of surprises! Father, who had waited so long for a male offspring, was so excited to learn of the birth of the third link in the family chain that he immediately cabled back his congratulations and said that he would soon be coming—to see for himself.

I find it difficult to describe our meeting—a father and his son, after many years of not having seen one another, each pained with so many memories and a long separation. My eyes filled with tears, and so did my father's. We faced each other wordlessly. My father suddenly seemed like a stranger, and he himself couldn't utter a sound. How were we to bridge these long years?

It was Dalit who broke the thick ice, in her own simple and straightforward way. "Grandpa," she said to Father, "do you know that Gal resembles you? Like two drops of water!" Father's wrinkled face lit up as I translated Dalit's remark. All of us were now at ease.

"I want to see him," Father whispered in French, looking at Dalit. "You really think he looks like me? And he will call me—*Saba*? That's a nice word—*Saba*."

Father gazed at the infant with glowing eyes. "You really think he looks like me?" he repeated. "A magnificent baby. I think he looks like you, my dear—very handsome." I translated, and Dalit's face sparkled with pleasure.

I saw nothing unusual in the red-faced, smelly infant— not in the beginning, at any rate. But Father fell in love with him at first sight. I guess you have to be a "veteran" father to find beauty in so young an infant. My father was a veteran all right: seven children and twenty grandchildren.

"Look at him," he would say, his eyes shining. "He is really handsome. A true member of the Cohen household. If only your mother were alive to enjoy it."

Father was with us in the kibbutz for a whole week. Then—well, it was Dalit's idea; I would never have thought of it. "Why don't you come and live with us?" she said to Father one evening. "Uri and I would love it, and so would Gal." I was sure that he would refuse, but he said that he would think about it. Perhaps . . .

When he said, "Good-bye, I'll be back," I didn't think he meant it seriously. But that's how it was. Father went back to Morocco, sold his business, and, half a year later, came to make his home in Israel, in Kibbutz Hadarim. He was given a room not far from the nursery and spent many hours, every day, with his grandson.

A deep affection developed between the two—the

blue-eyed, mischievous baby and the dark-browed old man. Little Gal softened the tough and stubborn man— he actually melted his heart. Gal did something to me, too. *I* became a better son. Now that I understood better, my attitude towards my father changed. I was no longer afraid of him, and the relationship between us became very close, as it had never been before. We used to talk a good deal about the old days. "How could you leave me, just like that?" he kept asking. I realized now what a terrible thing I had done, then. What if my son were to leave me? I shuddered at the thought.

"Taboul, Taboul!" Father would grip my hand, as if afraid that I would leave him again. I didn't mind his insistence on calling me 'Taboul' instead of 'Uri'. I was no longer ashamed of that name.

I now had two worlds: the new world of Israel— the divers, Dalit and Gal and the kibbutz, where I was Uri, Lieutenant Uri—and the old world overseas, where I left my sisters and Rosa and a host of friends behind. All these years I tried to keep from thinking about this other world and to stifle my longing. But now there was a change—Father was with me, my sisters began writing, and my memories were allowed to dwell on the past. I now had a very large family, in Morocco and all over Israel.

Assaf married Ora, a kibbutz girl, and added a sister-in-law to the family. Later came a niece, Michal. It gave me a wonderful feeling, to belong to such a large tribe.

My only regret was that Rosa didn't live to see my

good fortune. She died after a long illness which kept her bed-ridden for over a year. I shed many tears at the news. She had been like a mother to me. I was sorry not to have taken proper leave of her, years ago, and for the pain and grief I caused her when I left.

A year or two passed. Gal grew nicely and became a sturdy child, quick of tongue. Father struggled to learn Hebrew so that he would be able to talk with his grandson. I devoted my time to the divers. Step by step, I climbed up the ranks of command. Now I was the bearded commander, sitting behind the table and reviewing the files of the trainees. I was now the one to set up probations, to give lectures, to warn, to clap one trainee on the back and to dismiss another. I spent all day in camp, and in the evening I drove home to my family in the kibbutz, in the small car furnished by the navy.

I was elected to handle the absorption program of Kibbutz Hadarim. I knew how it felt to come to a strange, new place, without knowing the language and having no roots here, and I now did everything to make it easier for the new immigrants who came to the kibbutz. I was an old-timer now, yet I never forgot the lessons of the past.

After years of separation, I renewed the ties with my friends in the training group. Of all who came to Israel, only about half remained. The others were scattered; some returned to Morocco and some wandered off to other parts of the world. But those who didn't give up and, like me, decided to fight for their place here and to overcome all hardships—they took root.

Up to now I had kept away from them and from the past, but now that I was strong and self-assured in my new world, I had no fear. Everything was really like a story book. I was happy with my life and achievements.

Then came the spring of 1967. I shall never forget those days of preparedness, before the Six-Day War. In one stroke, everything was shaken: "Nasser is gathering his forces in Sinai! The Arab armies have signed a military pact against Israel." The fear of war was everywhere.

I knew that the outbreak of war would take the divers to the front line, to carry out assignments the way we had been taught—and for which we had drilled for so many years.

Twelve

Two sharp siren wails cut through the noon stillness of the sea, followed by thunderous orders issued over the entire public address system of the submarine: "Down and under!" The men on lookout came down and slid nimbly through the narrow, round opening.

I heard the click of the locking lever as it closed the sub's opening, and the air outflow. My ears felt the growing pressure. The sub dropped down towards the sea bottom, the floor of the vessel sloping towards the bow. We could hear clearly the slapping of the water against the bridge. The small portholes were sprayed with water, and sudden darkness descended upon us. We were down in the deep. The sub leveled itself and proceeded south, towards Egypt. Every member of the crew and every diver was at his station. The entire sub hummed with activity: the engines were roaring, the dials of the various gauges spun about and the signal apparatus was clicking sharply.

I stepped toward the periscope—the underwater eyes of the submarine. The air was very heavy. The yellow electric bulbs could not dispel the deep gloom. It was hard to believe that a few yards above us the noon hour was blinding bright with summer sun. Inside it was night—long and stifling. The round tube of the periscope went up. Major Shahaf, commander of the submarine, put his right eye against the round lens and peered out. He turned the periscope handles left and right and studied the surface carefully.

"You're in luck!" he said to me. "The sea's like a pool. Want to have a look?"

He stepped back and went off to the chart room. I bent towards the large, round instrument. Beyond the polished glass, with its two crossed lines, the sea looked blue and tranquil, from one end of the horizon to the other. It was hard to believe that not very far away, bitter fighting had been taking place on all fronts ever since morning.

This was Monday, the fifth of June, 1967. We were on our way to carry out a commando operation in an Egyptian port. I stood there, glued to the lens, for some time.

"Major Yiftah, Captain Uri—to the commander, to the commander!" an order blared suddenly through the loudspeaker in the corner. "Captain Uri"—the years had gotten me used to my name and title. I straightened up and hurried to the cabin of the submarine commander. I had been waiting tensely for this call since morning. Now we would get final instructions—the time of the operation and coordination with the submarine.

Yiftah was already in the commander's quarters when I arrived. Both were bent over a map spread out on a table that was used for eating and also doubled as a desk. Under it was a chest for personal belongings and next to it a sleeping cot. There was nothing luxurious about the submarine's accommodations.

"Look here, Uri," said Major Shahaf, adding new circles to those sketched out on the map, which was already marked with circles, arrows and winding lines. To anyone not familiar with such matters, it looked like a strange riddle, but to me it was plain and simple. The various markings indicated depth, currents, ports and shorelines.

"We'll be letting you off here," Major Shahaf said, noting a red dot on the map. "From this point, you'll have to swim the rest of the way. The submarine will be resting on the sea floor. We'll then wait for you here"— he indicated a green dot—"at two in the morning. If something happens and you don't make it back at two, we'll be back the next night, same time and place. Any questions?"

I remained bent over the map, studying the lines, dots and arrows. There were no questions; everything was clear. We knew exactly what our assignment called for. We had drilled and practiced it time and again during the last few years. Now the time had come for the real thing.

"If you have no questions," said Major Shahaf, "I'd advise you to have your crew get some rest. We still have several hours before we reach our destination."

We left the commander's compartment and made our way to the crew's quarters. It was very crowded here. We had to flatten ourselves against the corridor wall in order to let someone pass. Aboard the sub, we used the "warm bed" system. The cots were always occupied, as one shift would be on duty and the other asleep. We looked for vacant cots.

"Over here, fellows," came Yossi's voice. "We kept a couple for you." The cots in the narrow compartment were attached to the wall, one above or alongside the other. A long, narrow board ran between them; when this was used as a dining table, the cots served as benches. Right now, the beds were being occupied by our crew: Yossi, Buki, Assaf and Amos.

"Good men—every one of them," I thought, as I looked at them. All of us were senior divers, very well-trained and expert in our jobs. I had complete faith in this crew, especially with Yiftah, the highly-respected and capable "sea wolf" as our commander.

Yiftah, my former boss in the navy, whom I had first met when I decided to join the divers unit, was, to me, more than just a respected leader. We had become close friends. I thought that I knew him well, but somehow he always managed to surprise me. He did it again when he volunteered to head our unit. Yiftah had been separated from operational tasks and was now an adjutant in the naval command, but when the crisis of 1967 came, following the concentration of troops in Sinai and the blockade of the Straits of Tiran, he immediately returned to the front line, ready for action, as always.

Haim, the chef aboard the submarine, brought us our lunch. The food was always excellent, and we demolished it in good fashion, garnishing it with small talk in order to keep our minds from what awaited us.

"Wait until you see what I'm making for supper," grinned Haim. "Something special for you before you go."

"The restaurant aboard this tube," said Assaf, "is the best in the region."

In the colorless routine of the submarine, food was one of the few excitements. Three meals a day meant three things to look forward to, each day. We never knew what dish the chef was going to whip up. I was sure that, this evening, we were going to have something really extraordinary—and I was right.

Once the hearty meal was over and the dishes removed, we converted our benches to cots. I lay on my back, covered with a thin blanket, and tried to fall asleep. But sleep didn't come easily. I turned off the lamp above me and remained awake in the darkness. All around me commands kept echoing from the loudspeakers: "Note direction—six-seven-zero-zero! Thirty left! Helm all the way left! Forward! Three thousand each side!"

I felt the surge forward, southward, toward the enemy harbor. Steps sounded in the corridor, commands filled the air—these were the normal sounds aboard a submarine. I couldn't fall asleep, not so much because of the noise as because of my thoughts. They racked my brain and gave me no rest. I knew that we would carry out our assignment. We would get into the enemy harbor under the very noses of their coastal guard— despite searchlights, lookouts, barrier nets and other obstacles! We would attach mines to the enemy warships and missile boats in port. We would sink them, or send them flying into the air. I was sure that our crew would do all this. My doubts were about coming back. The submarine would be waiting for us outside the harbor, on the bottom of the sea. We would have to get out of the harbor and make our way to it; the sub could not come to us. The slightest movement, a careless sound, a few water bubbles—would be enough to betray us. This would mean being trapped in an enemy port— six against many, one knife against machine-guns, rifles and depth bombs.

The possibility of our not being able to make it back weighed heavily upon me. I knew that I must not give the fellows the slightest inkling of what was bothering me. I had to appear strong, smiling, confident. But in the darkness, with all the others asleep (or were they also awake, having the same thoughts?), I gave my thoughts free rein. Ten years had gone by since my arrival in Israel. The path had been rough and strewn with obstacles, but once I overcame them I found good fortune. I thought about Dalit, my wife for the past four years.

I glanced quickly at my watch. In the small square date-box glowed the number 5. June fifth! It was our wedding anniversary! That's a fine day for it—the first day of the war! How long will this war last and how many lives will it demand? I knew that, at this very moment, fierce armor battles were going on in Sinai. The Jordanians were shelling Jerusalem and some coastal points had been bombed. We heard about this before submerging. What else has been going on since then? I thought about my three-year-old Gal, who had made me a father and brought my own father back to me.

Who needed this war, anyway? Everything was going so nicely. Once I had thought that a "happy ending" could be found only in the movies, but life showed me that it does happen, in reality. It might have, now, were it not for this war. How would we return from it? Would it be in conditions of peace? Here we had to steal into an enemy harbor, swim about for an hour, bomb and wreak havoc and then swim back to the submarine. I held out no great hopes for success.

I forced my eyes to close, and immediately I saw Dalit, all smiles, holding little Gal as he called: "Daddy! Daddy! Come to me, Daddy . . ."

"We'll show them. They won't get anywhere near Israel's shores to hurt you," I said silently. "Don't worry, Dalit. Everything will come out all right."

I knew that, finally, I would have to fall asleep and gather strength for the assignment. I wanted to sleep and to stop thinking about the way back. It was now three in the afternoon. Yiftah's snoring came from the corner. I marveled at him: how could he sleep so restfully? Sleep . . . sleep . . . don't think . . .

I don't know when I fell asleep or how long I slept. Suddenly I felt someone shaking me. I awoke instantly.

"Yes, I'm up," I muttered. Yiftah's grinning face was above me.

"In another hour we'll arrive—and then we'll have to leave the tube," he said. "We better start getting ready."

Night fell, although in a submarine there is no difference between day and night. Here there is always a stuffy gloominess mixed with the yellow of the light bulbs. The engineers in the engine room were bent over their complicated motors and gauges; their overalls were greasy, like their hands and sweat-covered faces. The large, cylindrical torpedoes were in place. The periscope rose every once in a while to scan the outside darkness with its glass eye. The radar screen was attuned to any movement above us.

The divers now sat at the narrow tables and ate their supper. Haim really outdid himself. The aroma of the dishes he prepared was enough to arouse the most sluggish appetite—but not mine. I tasted a bit of everything, and that was all. Our communications officer had received word that enemy air strength had been destroyed and that we were advancing on all fronts. Would we be as successful?

We rose and went to dress. We got out of our clothes mechanically. This was no easy matter, in the cramped quarters aboard the sub, in the heat and dampness. We first put on khaki uniforms made of thin synthetic fabric. These uniforms, which dry quickly and need no pressing, would make it easier for us to hide in case we had to go ashore in enemy territory; we would take off our rubber suits, hide or destroy them, and try to mingle with the local population. Also, if we were caught, these uniforms would give us the status of prisoners of war, subject to the protection of the Geneva Convention. At that time we were still naive enough to believe that the rules of the Geneva Convention were being obeyed everywhere in the world, so that the khaki gave us a feeling of some security.

We donned our diving suits over the uniforms, as

we had done countless times. But the breathing apparatus and the other items we now received were the equipment of the attacking diver; they were not the same that we had used in practice, but to us they made little difference. The difference was that—this time—we stood a chance of losing not points but our liberty, and perhaps even our lives.

On the floor beside me were the limpet mines which I was to attach to the bottom of vessels in the harbor. We received our rations in a small can, as well as a flashlight, communications gear, maps and of course the vital knife secured at the ankle.

"Why don't you eat something?" wailed Haim, gazing at our half-filled plates. But none of us was very hungry that evening, nor did we want to go out on a full stomach. A diver standing off to one side watched us with concern and softly recited verses from Psalms.

"Psalms are a wonderful thing," commented Yossi, always in high spirits. "Psalms will never let you down." I saw that other divers were also joining in—fellows who had hardly ever prayed before. Now they prayed to the Almighty to help them return to the submarine in safety. I was sure that the divers themselves would do everything to carry out their mission—and more.

"Major Yiftah, Captain Uri," came the metallic voice over the loudspeaker. "To the commander."

"Already?" I wondered, as we hurried along the narrow corridor. "I thought we had at least another half hour before leaving."

We passed by the machines, the engines, the gauges—a jungle of metal and numerals.

Major Shahaf was again bent over the map spread on the table, as he had been when we left him at noon. I wondered whether he had been in that position all afternoon, without sleeping. His eyes were amazingly clear, though I knew that he had not slept the night before. The sub had been at sea ever since the emergency preparedness began, awaiting instructions from headquarters. Word came in the morning, along with the news about the outbreak of the fighting: "Bat, fly!" This was the signal for the six commandos aboard the sub, as well as to other frogmen units, to proceed with their assignments in the enemy harbor. We were now ready for it; all our equipment, by this time, was in the launching compartment. Had we arrived at zero hour?

"According to my tracking," said Major Shahaf, "the way is clear. I'll try to get the sub as close to the harbor as possible. That will make it easier for you."

Yes, I knew that everything would be made as easy as possible for us. This would endanger the sixty men on the sub; there were but six of us. But Major Shahaf knew what he was doing. The closer he got us to the harbor, the shorter would be the distance we would have to swim and the less energy we would have to expend. Anyway, it felt much safer aboard the sub.

I sat down at the periscope. All I could sense—rather than see—was darkness. The enemy harbor, somewhere on the horizon, was efficiently blacked out. The sky was studded with myriads of stars. The sub moved forward.

I was still at the periscope when the siren went off.

There's something frightening in the sound of a siren aboard a submarine, as though someone had seen you before you became aware of him and now has you in his sights, ready to fire.

"The commander to the tower!" echoed the call. "I saw something suspicious on the screen. I suspect an approaching craft."

"Right," checked the sonar man. "A destroyer."

"Battle stations," came the order. Every man ran immediately to his post.

"Dive deep," came Major Shahaf's voice, terse but calm. "Everything forward! Emergency! Full helm left!"

An air flow came from the chamber where the weight tank was being filled for the descent of the sub. The submersible began to go down—a slow descent, pushing its tons of steel to the safety of the deep. The periscope was down; now nothing on the surface was visible. Everyone stood by, alert and watchful.

"Prepare the sub against depth charges!" came the order through the loudspeaker. "Prepare for silent cruising."

"What's our depth?" I asked the seaman at the depth gauge. He gave the glass a slight rap to make sure that the gauge had not snapped.

"Passing seventy feet," he replied.

This wasn't deep enough, I knew. Depth charges released from a ship could severely injure a submarine— crack it, silence its engines, even sink it.

"Dive quickly! Everything forward! Emergency!" Major Shahaf ordered again.

The command echoed through the internal telephone system. Now the hermetic doors, between the various sections of the sub, were ordered shut, so that if one section were hit, the water would not flood the entire submarine. One section! I shuddered at the thought of the men in each section, now sealed off from one another. We at the command station could hear the sound of the air valves operating the hermetic partitions. There was no longer any reason for maintaining silence. It was obvious that the destroyer had detected us; the awesome depth charge would be coming at us at any moment.

I put on a pair of earphones. I could hear the sound of the propeller of the approaching destroyer; it was coming nearer.

"Helm at center!" came the order, and the needle gently moved to the center and stopped there. Major Shahaf was trying to maneuver away from the destroyer. The sound coming through the earphones told me that the destroyer was directly above. Anything could happen, at any second. Inside the sub the tension was fever-high.

"*Vroom!*" We heard a long, terrible explosion. The sub shook as if caught in a storm. All lights went out at once.

"Emergency lights!" came the order. A thick, impenetrable darkness was all about us, as if we were in a cave that pressed in on us from all sides. What happened to the others? Had one of the sections been hit? Ours wasn't. All the levers and valves were shut tight.

"Emergency lights! Emergency lights, immediately!" the order was repeated. The lights went on, faint and murky, but at least we could see. The compartment looked as though an earthquake had hit it. Maps and papers were strewn all over the floor, glass was cracked and instruments lay scattered everywhere. Major Shahaf's face had a deep, bleeding scratch.

"Nothing serious," he commented, wiping the blood away with the palm of his hand. "Everything forward! Emergency!" he ordered.

The signal man picked up the hand telephone, under the firing board, pressed the button and got in touch with all the other sections. I breathed more easily as the voices came in from the other stations, each in turn, reporting that everything was *b'seder*—okay—just a few scratches, light bumps and bruises. Nothing serious.

"Slow and quiet cruising," ordered Major Shahaf. Suddenly all of the sub's motors went silent. The fans and air-conditioners stopped. There wasn't a sound inside the sub. The crew moved about, each man engaged in his own duties. The propellers hardly moved. The valves and all moving parts were still. We were now like all the other silent creatures of the deep. Directly above us, we could hear the noise of the destroyer's propellers, as it combed the area for us.

Was this how a fox felt when pursued by the hounds? It was certainly an uncomfortable feeling. Someone up there was trying to hunt us down, and we were trying to get away, unseen and unheard. Our orders were not to engage in battle. I was sorry that we couldn't dispatch a torpedo or two at the destroyer, but the sub's assignment was to get us to our target—nothing else. I could imagine the struggle going on inside Major Shahaf. But orders were orders.

"Vroom!" Repeated explosions shook the silent submarine. Everything swayed around me. I tried to catch hold of something to maintain my balance, but didn't make it. A moment later I was thrown to the floor. My head hit a solid object and everything went black.

When I opened my eyes, everything was spinning—faces and sounds, the noise of propellers; that meant that the sub was not damaged! Were we out of it? I

tried to rise, but strong hands held me down.

"Lie still," someone said. "You got a swell bump on your skull."

"Yossi!" I cried, recognizing the voice. "What's going on?"

"Nothing unusual. We got a hot shower," he replied with a wide grin. How did he manage to be so cheerful, at all times?

"They gave us a reception with a few gorgeous depth charges," he went on. "Nothing worse than a small fire in one of the compartments which was quickly brought under control. A few cracks in the periscope, a few bruised heads, hands and knees, plus your forehead."

"Where are we?"

"They tried to make it easier for us and gave us a push towards the harbor, but that didn't fit in with our plans," explained Yossi. "We went the other way, and that's all there is to it."

"Are we far away?"

"Quite a distance. I think we'll get there on horseback. Nothing wrong with that."

"Horseback" meant approaching the target on a contraption called a "pocket sub." This was eight feet long and two feet wide, with room for two people astride, like on a saddled horse. This miniature sub could proceed at three miles per hour—not a dazzling speed, but much better than the speed of a swimmer with only his fins to help him. The pocket sub could also submerge to a depth of fifty feet. It had another advantage; its detachable front section was filled with explosives and could be used in an operation as an additional mine, with greater destructive force than the limpet mine carried by the frogmen. On the other hand, this device could be detected more readily.

"When do we go?" I asked, still on my back.

"Soon. While you were out cold, the fellows went to work and put the sub in working condition. Pretty soon, our tube will come down and we'll go up, and I hope we don't meet up with another depth charge on the way."

"Let's go, then," I said, rising. "We'll probably be going out right away."

"Are you up to it?" asked Yossi, in a worried tone.

"Sure." My head spun a bit as I got up, but that was no reason for me to remain behind. A bruised forehead didn't count as a combat wound.

We moved along the narrow corridor to the launching compartment.

"Good luck!" the submariners called.

"What else? We don't accept anything else," replied Yossi.

"I have an account of my own to settle with them," I said, gingerly touching my forehead.

Yiftah came up. "O.K., fellows. Ready for the party?"

I was glad that Yiftah was our commander. If anybody could get us through the operation safely, it was he.

"Now that our air force has blasted their planes and our armor is speeding through their lines," Yiftah went on, "we'll show them what the navy can do."

This was a command and a challenge. We went up the rungs of the iron ladder to the round opening, pushed our bodies through and slid our three pocket subs into the water. Yossi, the last one out, carefully closed the cover. Despite the late spring weather, the water was ice cold. It penetrated my rubber suit and chilled me through and through.

We looked out on a black sea. The submarine submerged and we were alone. But we knew that it was there, below, on the sea floor, waiting for us to return after completion of our assignment.

We were now slightly more than a mile north of the light tower at the western basin of the enemy port. We headed in that direction astride our pocket subs. Yiftah and Amos led the way, followed by Yossi and Buki, with Assaf and me bringing up the rear. The small craft were submerged, as were our bodies; only our heads were above water.

I looked up. Had I seen a shooting star, I would have made a wish—to get home safely. But I knew that astrology would be of no help to us now. We had to do it on our own—we, the six of us. And somehow I had an odd feeling that we weren't going to make it . . .

Thirteen

The pocket subs were now half an hour away from the enemy's port. The luminous dials on my watch showed the time to be ten P.M. I knew that at that moment other frogmen units were making their way to other enemy ports. The code signal, "Bat, fly!" was issued to all the units at the same time, and it launched a full-scale attack on enemy battleships at their bases.

Ours was a veteran unit of regular servicemen and reserves, but as far as strength and ability and doggedness went we were right up there with the younger men. Yiftah, in hand-picking the members of his unit, was more concerned with experience than with age. Yiftah himself was well over thirty, but there weren't many younger men who could match his ability and endurance. Again, as I rode astride the pocket sub, I felt happy to be with this unit. Here "one for all and all for one" was an iron-clad rule. We could depend on each other, under any conditions and in all circumstances; this feeling gave us a great deal of confidence.

For no reason at all, as I rode through the black water I happened to think of Uzi. After all these years I was no longer bothered by the trouble I once had with him. No, he did not fit into this unit. How could I have questioned it, then? I would now be overcome with terror if Uzi, instead of Assaf, were sitting behind me—the same Uzi that I had once regarded as a hero.

Two weeks ago I had come across Uzi, for the first time since he left the unit. This was during the preparedness period, when I couldn't go home. Passing a billboard, I noticed an announcement of a lecture by "U. Leshem, of the Hebrew University, Lecturer on Undersea Archaeology."

The name meant nothing to me, but I decided to attend the lecture and relax a bit. I was also curious to see the iron-nerved people who could still pay attention to a lecture at a time of such great danger. I also wanted to see who had not yet been mobilized. As I expected, the audience consisted chiefly of girls, high school students and a few elderly people who were obviously hoping that undersea archaeology would relieve their "war nerves."

On the platform I beheld a well-built, square-jawed man, the picture of poise and self-assurance. I recognized him immediately—Uzi! He had grown older, of course—he was a man now, no longer a youth. He spoke easily and related many tales of the underwater world. For a brief moment his eyes rested on me, but I could see no hint in his face that he recognized his former comrade in the frogmen's unit. The audience listened to him with rapt attention, and Uzi really did a fine job. He spiced his lecture with exciting tales and anecdotes, of which he obviously had a rich store. He certainly found himself, I thought; he was still "diving," with colorful speech for a diver's suit and a halo of adventure to boot. After the lecture was over I debated with myself whether I should go up to him. I decided against it. Better that way; let him be happy in his own world, without any disturbing memories of the past—as far as I was concerned.

At any rate, pushing on to an enemy port on the back of a pocket sub, I was truly glad that it was Assaf, and not Uzi, behind me.

All around us the sea was silent. The shore and the harbor, ahead, were completely blacked out, but we could see part of their silhouette against the lights of the city and villages beyond.

The silence was suddenly shattered by a salvo of shots from the direction of the harbor. I was sure that we hadn't been seen. The barrage must have been a safety measure, activated every once in a while to keep unwelcome intruders away from the area. The mysterious submarine which the enemy destroyer had detected an hour earlier must have also added to the state of tension on shore. We could see the dark shapes of boats crossing the mouth of the harbor, probably dropping depth charges. One of the shells fired from the shore came near enough to rattle our bones.

"Down!" ordered Yiftah.

We went under. Shells kept exploding overhead. The blasts themselves could be very dangerous when you're all exposed, protected by nothing more than darkness and the water surrounding you. The fire power of the bombs was tremendous. Did they think that they were being attacked by a whole fleet of submarines?

Or perhaps a brigade of commandos? The amount of explosives from the shore batteries certainly indicated that the famous Arabic imagination was working overtime. How we managed to survive all those blasts is something I shall never know. Pure luck, no doubt.

The coast guard cutters kept combing the black water. We could hear the sound of voices above us, but we remained unseen. The long, tough drills of bygone years were now paying off.

Again the harbor sank into silence. Powerful searchlight beams took the place of the artillery, criss-crossing the harbor area. We were already at the mouth of the harbor, but getting through was quite another matter. Thick protective nets, we knew, were stretched across the entrance, from a certain depth to the bottom of the sea, which was strewn with mines. The nets were intertwined with electric cables, equipped with all kinds of warning devices. Above the nets there was a passage lane, no more than 30 yards wide, for surface ships to pass through; this was controlled by a metal gate which reached down, in the water, to the top of the netting. We could dive down and try cutting through the netting, or—

A signal flash from shore told us that a ship was about to enter the harbor, during the lull in the barrage. This meant that the gate, operated electrically from the control building on the pier, would soon slide open. I positioned the pocket sub in the center of the 30-yard lane. The ship passed a few yards above us, causing our pocket sub to rock violently from side to side. I clutched the rudder stick and kept the sub going beneath

the hulk of the vessel overhead, with Assaf holding
on grimly to my waist. A bad move, and both of us
would slip off the sub and remain on the outer side
of the harbor.

My heart was pounding. Could we make it? We had drilled for this very maneuver many times in the past, but the real thing was somehow different. The noise from the ship's engine room was deafening, but we hung on—and made it. We kept in the wake of the vessel, almost under its rudder, and glided in past the huge gate, which immediately closed behind us.

We now had to make contact with the others. We dropped deeper and headed for the meeting place, a little-used loading pier at the end of the harbor. The others hadn't arrived yet, and we had no choice but to wait. At such a time—just before a major operation—waiting wasn't the easiest thing in the world. The minutes dragged on, and our concern for the others grew.

"I can hear them coming," Assaf whispered. He had unusually keen ears. A moment later Yossi and Buki came up, astride their sub. The backlash of the ship had wrenched the little contraption out from under them, and they barely had time to capture it and get in before the gate clanged shut.

"We set a record," whispered Yossi, "or something. Anyway, all future drills should include a runaway pocket sub moving away in an opposite direction from a moving ship."

Yossi's words were a bit mixed up, but my mind was on something more important. "What about the others?" I asked. "Did they make it under the ship?" With Yiftah still missing, I, his second-in-command, had to take charge. There was nothing we could do but wait some more. A good hour later Yiftah and Amos arrived, under their own power. Their little sub was caught in the netting and could not be removed. The two expert frogmen went down to the sea floor and, after dismantling the warning device there, lifted the netting, crawled under and swam to the meeting place.

Dismantling these warning devices is no easy task. It calls for supreme skill, long practice and iron nerves. Unless the entire section is dismantled, the alarm would sound if the netting were to be lifted by so much as a few inches. Yiftah was an expert in this operation. I felt grateful for being part of such a superb team.

Now all of us were together. The barrage went off again; the enemy was extremely nervous. We could hear all the activity going on above us, along the piers. Again every inch of the port and the entire harbor was being combed. We could see the dark shapes of the cutters streaking across the black water. We could even hear the footsteps of the sentry on the pier, not more than two yards above us. When he was gone Yiftah outlined the plan: we would leave the two pocket subs under the pier, since we could move about more freely without them. If we could use them later in making our escape—so much the better, otherwise we would have to swim for it.

We made the miniature subs secure, then tightened our helmets. Yiftah's thumb went up: "Ready? Frogmen—down and under!" We went down, each pair heading toward its assigned target. I don't know how the tank soldier feels inside his Sherman or the pilot in his Mirage, but our feeling was something different. All you have to do is raise a few bubbles, make a splash, even swim too vigorously—and that's it; you're through.

We swam on, under the cover of darkness, guided by the needle of the compass strapped to our wrists, shining in the pinpoint of light provided by our pencil-thin flashlights.

Assaf and I were now at the spot where our map showed the location of our first target: we were to blow up the missile boat "Star of the Winds." We swam the entire length of the pier, but the boat wasn't in its regular berth. We moved on to our other targets; they weren't where they were supposed to be, either. We were in a quandary. Even with all the merchant and passenger vessels anchored in the area, we should have found our targets by this time. Where could they have disappeared? The only explanation that I could think of was that the enemy had removed his "fighting" ships to the safety of some distant port. (Later we found that this was exactly what happened).

It was now past midnight. This meant that the submarine wouldn't be able to wait for us much longer. It had to leave the area before dawn or else run the risk of being discovered. If we would leave immediately, we might still get back in time to be picked up. On the other hand, how could we return without having carried out the tasks assigned to us? Positively not! I couldn't discuss this with Assaf in the water, but I knew that he felt exactly as I did. If we couldn't do it now, we would have to get back to the submarine on the following night—but only if our job were done. At dawn we would have to find some hiding place along the beach and come back after dark. This, too, would be dangerous, but we had no other way.

We were now in the water for over three hours, plus another hour spent in fruitlessly scouring the harbor for our targets. I was hoping that Yiftah and the others were having better luck. If they had found their targets and attached their mines, then they would certainly be back at the meeting place—worrying about *us*.

The long search was wearing us down. Our bodies were half-frozen from the ice cold water. I tugged at the line and signaled to Assaf to surface. We inflated our belts and came up under one of the piers.

"I'll climb up on the pier and try to spot the targets from there," Assaf said.

This was a terribly risky thing to do. The first signs of dawn would soon be visible in the eastern sky. A diver usually doesn't show himself during daylight. But, we both agreed, an enemy diver walking along the pier would be the very last thing the Egyptians would expect to see.

Assaf raised himself to the edge of the pier, glanced about and climbed up. I remained where I was, the rope dangling from my wrist, listening intently. But the harbor was silent. The only sound came from the east: muffled artillery fire. That's where the fighting was going on, and the sounds meant that our forces were well inside Egyptian territory. Good, I said to myself; the Egyptians forced this war upon us—let them now have a taste of life in the air raid shelters.

Now I was sorry that I let Assaf go, alone. It was sheer madness. What would I tell his parents—and Dalit? He was my best friend, not only my brother-in-law. I decided to climb up and look for him.

Just then I heard the sound of running feet, a soft swish of water, and Assaf was back at my side.

"The cowards!" he whispered, breathing hard. "They took every one of their boats out of the harbor. Not a single battle craft is left."

That's one way of fighting a war, I thought. "Where did you go?" I asked. "Did you meet up with anyone?"

"Not even a stray dog," replied Assaf, in disgust. He tied his end of the rope back to his wrist. "What

do we do now?"

"We should get rid of our explosives—plant them somewhere, so that our mission won't be a total loss." But very little time remained now.

"I have an idea," said Assaf. "They got all the boats out of here, but they couldn't remove the buildings and installations. At the end of this pier I saw a large building that looks like command headquarters; it's practically on the water. I'm sure there are documents and maps inside. It's close enough for us to blast it before daylight. What do you say?"

"Blast it?" I repeated. "The limpet mines are good enough for blowing holes in the bottom of a ship, not in a building."

"What about the caps of the pocket subs we detached?" Assaf reminded me. "There should be some use for that load of explosives."

"Fine," I agreed. "Let's get going."

We deflated the belts, put on our masks, checked the tanks and went under. Our target now was the white building at the other end of the long pier. The water became quite shallow and we had to crawl on our stomachs to reach the spot. In daylight our black suits would have showed up beautifully against the light sand and bleached rocks, but we prayed for the night to linger just a few minutes longer—like Joshua prayed when he came to Canaan and ordered the sun and the moon to wait a while.

We covered the last few yards slowly, inching our way along the sharp rocks; I could feel them scratching through my rubber suit. The windows in the building loomed above us like square black spies, watching every move we were making.

We planted our explosives at the base of the building, just where one corner jutted into the water. The charge wasn't strong enough to demolish the entire building, but we were prepared to settle for a healthy blast. We just didn't want our mission to be a total loss.

This done, we crept back to the water. It was easier now, without the weight of the explosives, but moving with our backs to the enemy was something we didn't relish. We could hardly wait until we were back in deep water. Now, with no contact with the others, we would have to make our way out of the harbor and find a cave in which to hide until nightfall, and then swim out to our rendezvous with the submarine.

We swam beneath the surface. Above us we could see the light of day and the shadowy shapes of vessels sailing in the harbor. We proceeded by compass to the spot where Yiftah had dismantled the warning devices. The entire area was a maze of netting strung on a jungle of steel poles. Here was the spot—east by northeast— where we should lift the netting off the sea floor and slip out from under. We first considered wriggling through the rings which joined the sections of the netting. I might have done it at one time, when I was a slim boy, but now my body, though by no means stout, was too big. Both Assaf and I had definitely outgrown the rings.

We finally found the spot where Yiftah had gone through, but there were still the mines and electric cables to avoid—and we were dead tired. A cable dangled in front of me, curling around the netting. All I had to do was to swim around it, but I didn't see a single warning device attached to it. I decided to raise it a bit for Assaf to go through, then he would do the same for me. But as soon as I lifted the cable—which no fish could do—I felt it vibrating strongly and I immediately realized that I had committed a horrible act—I set off the alarm!

Fourteen

It took no more than an instant for the alarm to throw the entire port area into an uproar. Sirens wailed and whistled all over the harbor. What was worse, the alarm also showed where it had been triggered, and in no time at all cutters came tearing in our direction from all sides. Scores of Egyptian frogmen, knives drawn, dived from the boats and surrounded us. Hardly able to move, we rose to the surface and were met with a hail of bullets spattering all around us, just in case we had any notion of trying to escape. We swam to a nearby buoy, removed our masks, and held our hands high, breathing heavily with fatigue.

"This is the end of the road," muttered Assaf. I was too tired to wonder what he meant, but something told me that the chances of our ever getting back were very, very slim.

The cutters formed a ring about us. Beneath us were the frogmen, watching our every move. Why did all this suddenly seem so familiar? Yes, I now recalled that I had seen this action in a movie, when I was a young boy—the movie that aroused my desire to be a diver. But I was far from resembling the hero of the story; I wasn't going to overcome my enemies single-handedly and return home safely. That was strictly for the movies.

For some reason the boats held off from approaching us. Perhaps they thought that we were some kind of a secret weapon. Finally they edged closer, carefully, suspiciously.

"Good, wonderful, so you got us!" Assaf called out. "We're your prisoners."

I repeated his words in Arabic, careful not to make the slightest false move. To our captors we seemed to be creatures from another planet, dangerous beyond words, rather than two unarmed and worn out men who had spent an entire night in the water. We were the all-powerful foes, and the slightest move on our part could bring on total disaster.

Perhaps it was the fact that I spoke their tongue which broke the spell. Now brimming with confidence, they dragged us savagely into one of the boats, kicked us and spat in our faces.

I managed to keep my feet. "We're prisoners of war and we demand that we be treated as such," I called out to the seaman who seemed to be the leader.

His reply was a resounding slap which I took on my cheek. "Prisoners!" he yelled. "You are sons of dogs! You are the brood of Satan! We'll show you!" Again blows were rained upon us.

I thought of the others. If they waited for us at the spot where we agreed to meet, inside the harbor, then they would also be trapped. On the pier, as the coast guard cutter drew near, I could see a crowd milling

about. Shouts filled the air. Was this our welcoming committee? I tried to catch a word, but all I could hear was the ugly sound of a howling mob. But as we drew near, a boy came running to the edge of the water. He pointed to the mob behind him and yelled shrilly:

"*Yahood! Yahood!* (Jews! Jews)."

"They've caught the others," I whispered to Assaf.

"Shut up!" yelled one of the guards, kicking me in the thigh.

The mob was in a frenzy. Barefoot fishermen, beach-combers, stones and knives in their hands, had ringed the four divers, waiting for someone to make the first move to massacre them.

I was familiar with the character of the Arabs from my own childhood days in Morocco. I knew that I had to act quickly, before someone made that first murderous move, The mob was enjoying the feeling of having the *Yahood* at its mercy; seeing their blood flow was to be the main performance.

"Those are my men," I said to the uniformed commander of the cutters. "I demand that you treat them as prisoners of war!"

"Why don't you go ahead and say this to the people?" demanded the officer, with an evil grin. "Let's see how much influence you have on them."

I didn't know what I was going to do, but the officer's words at least let me do something, instead of standing by helplessly. I jumped up to the pier. As I pushed my way through the mob, I suddenly recalled the image of my father, standing up to a mob about to loot his store, right after the Sinai campagn in 1956.

"Another one! Another one!" the mob greeted my appearance. "Massacre the Jews!" One or two tried to grab me as I pushed past.

"Take your hands off me!" I shouted in my most imperious tones. It worked. A sudden hush fell over the bloodthirsty throng. I don't know what impressed them more—the bold tone of my voice or my fluent

Arabic; anyway, that I, of the *Yahood,* should be giving orders to them was unbelievable.

I finally pushed my way to the center of the ring. The four were bruised and bleeding. From the corner of Yiftah's mouth came a thin trickle of blood. Buki's eyes were blackened and his suit was torn. Amos was stretched out on the cobblestones, with Yossi bending over him.

"Uri!" exclaimed Yiftah. "So you're our savior! Another minute and our throats would have been slit."

"We're not out of it yet," I muttered. And, indeed, we weren't. The mob, seeing us talking together, came to life. The circle began to close in.

"Order them to stop!" I yelled to the coast guard officer. "We're prisoners of war. The entire world will know that you are savages who murder prisoners."

"Yes," chimed in Assaf, standing next to the officer. "People will say that you are—" and he added a string of insults, which was the usual Arabic vocabulary of a *kibbutznik.*

This time the officer was impressed. Public opinion was something to consider. He took a step toward the mob, holding up his submachine gun, but I could see that he did not relish his task.

"I—I'll shoot!" he shouted, but his voice was lost in the growl of the mob.

He raised his gun and fired a burst into the air. The mob fell silent and parted to let him through. He advanced stiffly, slowly, keeping one eye on the mob and the other on us. "Lie down," he said to us. "Lie down on the ground, all of you. I'll protect you."

"He wants us to lie down," I translated for the others. "Don't do it. This will show that we're afraid, and that's just what the mob is waiting for."

We remained on our feet. Yossi helped Amos raise himself from the ground and held him up; Amos had suffered a severe blow on the head. We stood there, together with the hesitant soldier and his weapon, hemmed in by the mob. I had no idea what to do next, but Yiftah saved the situation. Just as I was beginning to lose all hope, he took a step toward the leaders of the mob and yelled at them, in English:

"We are Russian officers," he cried. *"Russki, Moscovi.* Your friends. You will pay dearly for all this."

A murmur ran through the crowd.

"We are Russians, *Russki, Muscovi,*" repeated Yiftah. "We are here to engage in secret practice drills. I demand that we be taken to naval headquarters."

The word *Russki* did the trick. The ignorant mob didn't know the difference between Russian and English. *"Russki, Moscovi,"* came excitedly from all sides. The faces of the people about us were still dark with suspicion, but their earlier rage had ebbed. The soldier began to prod us, with his gun, out of the thinning circle of the mob, towards a large building flying the Egyptian flag. We were thrust into a small chamber—a cell, really—with a barred window, and the door clanged shut behind us.

"Yes, sir," said Yiftah. "I didn't think we'd ever get out of that one.

"The bit about the Russians was pure genius," remarked Yossi. "Good that you didn't say Americans."

Yiftah had thought of that. "I was first going to say Englishmen, but at the moment I think Russians is more effective. I didn't even consider the Americans."

"Some shape I'm in," groaned Amos, holding his head. To tell the truth, we weren't much better off.

Yossi alone was equal to the occasion. "Gentlemen," he suggested, in a tone that the head waiter of a fashionable restaurant might use, "I invite you to dine." He reached inside his suit and brought forth a packet of the mud-like mess which, as we had been taught, was "good for divers." All the years in the navy I always detested this food, although it was packed with vitamins. But right now it tasted better than anything I had ever eaten.

"Some state of affairs," muttered Assaf, after we were done with the packet of concentrated nourishment.

"They removed our targets," remarked Buki. "That's what is eating me more than anything else. We wasted all our time looking for them, and even if we did plant explosives here and there—."

"Hey!" yelled Assaf. "That reminds me!"

Me, too. I began to shiver as I let the others know: "This is the building to which we attached our mines. They're set to go off at—" I glanced at my watch, but it was gone, as were the compass and the depth gauge; somebody in the mob had done an expert job. "I don't know exactly," I went on, "but the explosives will be going off in half an hour, at most."

We stared at one another in dead silence.

"We must keep away from the window," said Yiftah

tersely, "and lie down near the far wall. I don't think that the limpet mines will do much damage."

"We also planted the stuff from our pocket sub," added Assaf, unhappily.

Silently we moved away from the window to the far wall, waiting for the blast.

Buki broke the silence. "We should tell them about it," he urged. "Keeping quiet won't help us. They'll have to leave and take us along. We won't tell them when the blast is scheduled to come, and they won't have time to look."

Amos shook his head. "This won't help us at all," he said. "They'll go away and leave us here, to be blown up together with the building."

Yiftah didn't agree. We were too valuable a prize to let go, he insisted. We would be brought before their tribunal—and all of us knew what that meant.

"Then what do you recommend we do?" I asked Yiftah. I was glad that he was in command and would have to make the decision: to tell the Egyptians or to keep quiet. But before he had time to say anything, five soldiers burst into the cell, bound our hands and, guns held in readiness, shoved us out in single file towards a command car waiting outside.

Fishermen, passersby and street urchins stood around, hatred in their eyes, and watched us climb into the car. Suddenly the sound of explosions filled the air and, from the direction of the port, came flashes of fire and billowing smoke. A large vessel moored to the pier lurched, listed slowly to one side, then rapidly began to sink. Then came another explosion—and another. Our crew had done a fine job with the limited amount of explosives they had with them.

Would ours go off just as easily? I gazed at the large building with the Egyptian flag flapping in the breeze. My look acted like a lighted match in a gas-filled room. A blast—and the small window of our cell disintegrated in a cloud of dust and stone. A gaping hole showed in the wall.

"Jews! Massacre the Jews!" yelled the bystanders. We were clearly the culprits. From all sides people came running, shrieking, waving their daggers. But the soldiers had obviously been ordered to take us somewhere—alive. A detachment in a jeep behind the command car waded into the crowd, rifle butts swinging. The soldiers struck their countrymen almost with delight; women and children were hit along with the rest. But the mob wouldn't give up so easily. Dozens of hands gripped the sides of the car and shook it as though it were made of cardboard.

"Yalla! Yalla! Get going!" the officer in charge yelled to the driver. The latter threw the car into gear and plowed through the mob barring his path, leaving a trail of cursing and screaming Arabs in his wake.

I was astounded by the depth of their hatred for us. It had made animals out of them. In twenty years it had caused an entire people—a once proud and noble people—to turn into a hysterical mob. There had to be a way to dispel this hatred. But right now we had a war to win; everything else would have to wait.

We sat in the command car, each immersed in his own thoughts. These thoughts were probably the same:

what would happen when we would be face to face with the Egyptian interrogators. This was their chance to gain fame and glory—by forcing six captured enemy frogmen to tell all they knew.

The command car turned into the highway leading to the city. We drove through the suburbs and came out to the main streets; the showy stores, I noticed, had their windows taped. We finally came to a large stone building with all its windows barred. The soldier with the submachine gun who had saved us from the first mob looked at me and said, "Well, we are here." There was no hatred in his voice; I even detected a note of pity in it. He knew what was awaiting us—as did we. "Why did you have to get yourself into this mess?" his look seemed to say. I kept quiet. If he didn't know that we were fighting to remain alive, then my telling it to him would serve no purpose.

The officer of the unit ordered us to climb down. We were led up the broad front steps into a long corridor, which ended at a small, smelly room. The only light and air came through a small round window high up on the wall—just below the ceiling. We looked at one another.

"For the same money," said Yossi, grandly, "we can be seated."

The floor was covered with a jelly of mud and dirt. We remained standing.

"All I'm hoping," whispered Yiftah, "is that our submarine didn't wait for us too long." That was just like him; even though he was about to face torture, he was worried lest the sub had endangered itself and its crew by remaining at the spot in daylight.

"It's very risky," went on Yiftah, dropping his voice even lower. "The water there is not very deep, and a low-flying plane would surely spot it. They will also have to come up for air. I hope they weren't foolish enough to wait."

"What I'm dying to know," said Amos, "is how the war is going."

"We're winning, of course," declared Yossi. "Their air force was done away with yesterday. It's a matter of days."

Always the optimist, that Yossi. Buki thought the war would take about a month. I, always ready to see the darker side, thought it would last a bit longer, but I wasn't going to say it out loud. The main thing was that our side should win.

"You'll see," said Yossi. "Our men will get here and set us free."

"May your words reach the ears of the Lord," said Yiftah. "For the present, men, remember: be strong and be silent."

We knew this, of course. And, as if the tension in our little cell weren't enough, the air outside was alive with the sounds of explosion in the distance, the whine of jets overhead and the air raid sirens.

A cry of pain suddenly came from the other side of the wall. "They are torturing someone!" cried Amos. "The dirty—."

"Nonsense," interrupted Yossi. "They're playing a tape to frighten us." In the course of our training we had listened to miles of such tapes, in order to get used to the sound. But this cry was very real.

"They're coming!" said Amos, his ear against the door. We could hear the heavy steps, the clanking of a chain. Then a key turned in the lock.

"You there!" shouted the evil-faced jailer, pointing at Yiftah. "Move!" We wondered how he knew that Yiftah was our leader; none of us had any sign of rank on his person.

"Frogmen—down and under!" Yossi raised his thumb toward our commander. We all saluted, thumb up. Yiftah smiled and returned the salute.

As second-in-command, I should have been the next one to go. But when the door opened again, the jailer's finger pointed to Yossi. "Frogmen—down and under, to the lion's den!" was Yossi's jaunty comment.

I truly loved this Yossi—always ready with a good word in a bad spot. Slim, quick, fearless. And how I admired my commander, going bravely to the fate awaiting him on the other side of the door.

One of the soldiers stationed at the door hit Yossi with the butt of his rifle. Yossi went down to one knee.

"Lion's den? A jackal's lair!" he muttered, wiping away the trickle of blood from his nose. "Uri, ask them if that's the way they always treat prisoners. We might not let ourselves be taken next time."

Yossi's tone must have angered the soldiers. They struck him again and again, until he sank down to the floor, then grabbed him by his feet and dragged him out of the room.

"They killed him, those miserable cowards," whispered Amos.

"No, not Yossi," said Buki, under his breath. "He's too tough. Besides, he wouldn't give them the satisfaction."

There were four of us left. I stationed myself at the door and waited. But when the jailer came again, his entire manner was completely changed. "Tell your friends," he said to me, "that they shouldn't be difficult. They're making hash out of the other two. All of you better go along and save your skins." Seeing that I made no move to tell the others anything, the jailer spat at me, grabbed Assaf by the arm and yanked him out into the corridor.

"They're trying everything," I now said to Buki and Amos. "A soft tongue and a murderous whip. Remember, not a word." I didn't go into details; the cell probably had hidden microphones planted in the walls, and we were no doubt being watched from unseen windows. We had to be very careful.

Next came Buki's turn, then Amos was taken away. I was alone.

A long time passed, and I wondered why. I knew that my turn had to come. Perhaps we were just being put into solitary cells. As if in answer, cries of pain came at me from all sides. The sounds were being piped into the cell, for my benefit. I recognized the voices of my tortured companions. Had I been left for last because I knew Arabic—and could give them all the information they wanted?

I could have sworn that hours passed before I heard the sound of footsteps again. The jailer was back. He was grinning as though the most wonderful things in the world were happening all around him. "Come on, my dear fellow," he leered. "All your friends are on their way to the sausage factory. Now it's your turn." He smacked his lips, and the soldiers behind him laughed loudly.

How I hated those soldiers! I could still see Yossi sinking to the floor, under the rain of the rifle butts. Hatred and cruelty were their mark, and the two went along so well together. Their rifle butts were now poised to strike me, at the slightest pretext. I kept quiet and went ahead of the jailer.

The room where I now found myself was large and beautifully furnished—except for the soldiers who lined the walls. An immense portrait of Egypt's president hung on the wall, showing his white teeth. Beneath the portrait sat a mustached officer, toying with the engraved handle of a gleaming knife. He looked at me as a cat looks at a mouse which isn't going to get away. He said nothing at first, letting me listen to the groans that came from somewhere beyond the walls.

"Cursed spy!" he suddenly barked. I wondered how a human being could turn purple so quickly. Also, to my surprise, he spoke good Hebrew. "We know everything about the spy network you have set up in Egypt. We already have all the dirty Jews in Egypt in our power, and we shall massacre them to the very last one! And you Palestinian Jews aren't even ashamed to come here and make trouble for the Egyptian Jews! Today we shall begin putting them in front of the firing squads— all because of you, you spies without a soul! Tell me how you made contact with Egypt's Jews! How did you get here? How long have you been here? How many agents have you sneaked in by water? How many Americans are there among you? What posts do they hold?" He shot the questions at me without pause.

"I am not a spy," I said, as he ran out of breath. "I am a soldier, a diver in the navy. And a prisoner of war doesn't have to answer questions put by his captors."

"What did you say?" yelled the officer, his face going a shade more purple.

"I am a prisoner of war," I repeated. "I am ready to give you my name, rank, armed forces number—and that is all. Not another word."

"You're a spy!" screamed the officer behind the table. "All of you are accursed spies, not soldiers!"

"I am a soldier," I insisted.

He jumped up and came at me like a tiger, gripping the knife. With one slash he slit open the sleeve of my rubber suit.

"Aha!" he cried. "A soldier, eh? Dressed in civilian clothing underneath! You're a spy!" He drew back and signaled to the soldiers. They surrounded me on all sides and hammered me with their fists. I tried to defend myself as best as I could—as we had been taught (Dalit used to get upset at the sight of the black-and-blue marks which those drills left on our bodies). The blows were painful, but they didn't break me. I kept flexing my muscles, drawing them taut and easing them in turn. I pretended to lose consciousness in order to gain a moment of respite. Fortunately, the officer kept stopping the soldiers in order to ask another question or two. Then the beating went on again. I knew that my comrades were undergoing the same treatment in the adjoining rooms.

The officer finally had me brought to a chair in front of his desk. "I didn't want to make you feel bad," he began, with a sorrowful tone in his voice, as his cat's eyes kept watching my face, "but you might as well know the truth. It's all over. Our troops have overrun all of Israel. Yes, indeed; Tel Aviv is in flames! Not a soul there is left alive! This is your last chance to escape death. Tell us everything. Of course, you will have to spend some time in jail, but we won't put you in front of a firing squad. Later we shall release you, and you will be able to go abroad and start life anew. But if you won't talk, spy, you won't live to see another sunrise."

I knew that he was lying. The Egyptians were looking for an excuse to crush their own Jews, since they were powerless against Israel. Then again, if the Egyptians were really victorious, as he was boasting, why was he going to all this trouble? And why did he want me to say that Americans were helping Israel? Perhaps they were looking for an excuse to explain their defeat! I lay on the floor, where I had fallen off the chair, bruised and bleeding, pretending to be in a faint but happy inside. The Egyptian officer had as much as told me that we were winning!

"Get him up on his feet!" ordered the officer. I let myself droop between the two soldiers who were propping me up. "Talk!" he yelled. "Save yourself, you fool! Everything is lost!"

"My name is Uri Cohen," I mumbled, "and I am a captain in the Israel Defense Forces."

"Come on," his voice changed to pleading. "Don't be so stubborn. Your companions are not as foolish as you. They have told us everything, to the last detail. Your stubbornness will cost you your life."

Another lie. I knew that the others wouldn't utter a single revealing word. The enemy could beat us to death, but he wouldn't get out of us anything that we didn't want him to know. Jewish spy rings and Americans fighting alongside our forces—let them keep on imagining! Certainly we weren't going to tell them how we got there and how we expected to get back. The officer wanted to know how we were to make contact with the craft that brought us; he even had the soldiers drag me to a map on the wall and asked me to be good enough to show him, with just a tiny little dot, where this craft was supposed to be waiting to pick us up. He also wanted to know about our training methods—just to compare them with the Egyptian system, naturally.

This questioning went on all day and stretched into the night. Another officer was now behind the desk, but the questions were the same. So were the answers: my name, rank and number, plus the statement that, as a prisoner of war, I didn't have to say anything more. In time I couldn't utter anything.

Those were the most horrible twenty-four hours we ever spent. Near noon, on the following day, we were brought together. I shuddered when I saw them, bruised and battered.

"Do I look as bad as you fellows do?" asked Yossi, in a tone which dared us to tell him he did.

"Worse," replied Amos. Yossi was a sight. In his tattered rubber suit (one strip dangled behind him like a tail), and with his puffed face, blue in spots, he looked like a ragamuffin who had just come in from a street corner brawl.

"Are you in one piece, Yossi?" I asked anxiously. "Any bones broken?"

"Broken?" he snorted. "You know I have rubber bones; they bend a bit but they never snap."

We were able to talk because our captors were busy with further plans for us. We managed to let each other know that no one had given out any information.

The door opened and we were led out and into the command car. We were being taken back to the port, perhaps to have us show the Egyptians where and how we managed to attach the mines. Beyond the low houses we could catch glimpses of the beach, sailboats, beautiful summer homes with private bathing and boating areas. We were headed for more questioning, naturally. Perhaps the Israeli forces would capture the city and free us, I thought idly, just to keep my mind off what would eventually be our fate. No one could help us. We would carry on to the very end. Each one would have to bear up under the beating and the threats and the promises, without saying a word.

I sat opposite the soldier who seemed to have taken pity on us. Our eyes met, but I could see that he didn't dare make a move or utter a sound. He had dark sad eyes, and the look in them was what we call a "warm Jewish look." Well, I mused, both of us had the same ancestor, but how the family had drifted apart . . .

The guard next to me was enjoying our situation tremendously. He kept nudging me with his submachine gun and flexing his trigger finger. He suddenly turned to me, with a leer, and said, in Arabic: "Tell your friends that they are enjoying their last ride. Your end is near, miserable spies!" He moved his finger across his throat. "We'll butcher every single one of you!"

Fifteen

The houses along the busy highway grew fewer and
fewer. Sand dunes now covered most of the region
we were passing through. We were headed north, to
the sea.

The scream of air raid sirens suddenly erupted from
stations in the area. From the huts near the highway
people came running in terror, heading for the safety
of the dunes. The vehicles on the highway braked to
a halt and their occupants took to the ditch on the south
side of the road—as did our guards. Out of the blue
sky appeared a squadron of glistening planes, flying
in V-formation. They roared down to the highway
with an ear-splitting noise. Explosions shook the earth.
For a moment we panicked; that was all we needed—to
die on Egyptian soil, victims of our own planes!

"I didn't know that relations between our air force
and our navy were so bad," muttered Yossi.

"Fellows!" said Yiftah, above the din. "Jump, now!
This is our chance! We meet at that blue house, by the
sea. Let's go!"

This certainly was indeed our chance, with the guards
crouching in the ditch. We jumped out, keeping the

jeep between us and the soldiers, and plunged head-long across the dunes, toward the sea.

"Scatter!" order Yiftah. "Get to that house not later than nightfall!"

I tore off what still remained of my diving suit. It was all in strips and tatters, but our captors had insisted that we keep our suits on, probably to display us, the frogmen spies, on their television. I stopped long enough to bury the rubber suit in the sand and kept going in my khaki which, while not as neatly pressed as when I had worn it at other times, blended in with the sand and made me nearly invisible from the road. With my bare feet I looked like any other Arab, but this was little comfort as I plodded through the blazing sand. My mouth felt like cardboard. Besides, I hadn't eaten anything except the battle rations, more than a full day ago.

But this, I realized, was no time to give up. The blue house seemed to be quite a way off. I hoped that we would have the strength to get there. Overhead the Mirages were still circling, as though to let the Egyptians know who was in control of their skies. I felt a strong urge to straighten up and yell: "Hey, you up there! It's me, Uri! Help us get home!"

Well, they *were* helping us. Had it not been for their sudden appearance, we wouldn't have been able to escape. I saw them diving again, and from the direction of the port came loud blasts of bombs hitting home.

It was a good hour later when I came to within creep-ing distance of the house. I crawled forward, not knowing what to expect. To my delight, the other five were already there. While there was no sign of life inside the blue house, we decided to hide for the present in a shack some thirty paces away. Inside it was dark, and the place smelled of fish which had been out of the water for some time.

"We'll remain here until nightfall," said Yiftah, "then follow the beach until we find a sailing boat. We'll borrow it to get out of the area."

It was a daring plan, but none of us could suggest anything else. At the moment, our problem was food. Yossi volunteered to get into the house, despite the closed shutters. He returned about five minutes later with the report that there wasn't a living soul around. More than that, he brought back a pitcher of cold water, several dry *peetah* bread loaves and a dishful of chick-peas, dry but edible. We could now remain where we were until dark.

We decided to use the time for sleeping, in the gloomy shed. One of us remained as lookout, to be relieved at the end of one hour. We took turns, red-eyed and yawning. When Yossi woke me, I could swear that I hadn't been asleep for more then ten minutes; now I felt more tired than before. I kept fighting off the desire for sleep by moving my eyes from my friends to the sand and sea outside.

Suddenly I heard a voice—a child's laughter. Was it my Gal? My eyes were now wide open. Again I heard the sound of laughter. I crept to the doorway. A little Egyptian boy was perched on his mother's back, on the way to the house. He was very much like Gal, with laughing black eyes that knew nothing about war. He felt safe on his mother's back—but her eyes were not laughing.

I knew that we couldn't afford to be caught unawares, by anybody. I woke the others. We crowded near the doorway. The woman was going into the house.

"Is that where you got the food?" I asked Yossi.

"Sure! Food hasn't come down from heaven since the days of Moses. Why?"

I didn't answer. I was thinking of the little boy. Perhaps it was his food that we had eaten. What a thought—with war going on all around . . .

The sound of motors in the distance came to us. "They're looking for us," whispered Yiftah.

Five or six command cars, filled with soldiers, were heading toward the blue house. Yiftah was right. "To the sea," he ordered.

Fortunately, there was a slight drop, just behind the shed, to the beach. We crawled out of the shed and slid down. The voices behind us sounded very near.

The sensation of cold water made my body tingle with new vigor; here I was in familiar surroundings—and I knew how to handle the situation, as did all of us. From the shallow water we began swimming north, using quick, strong strokes. I took off my khaki shirt and tore it into strips, which I then bound around my head and face to lessen the chances of their being seen from shore. The others took the cue and did the same. Under other circumstances we would have found each other very funny indeed.

I took a quick glance at the beach. The soldiers were milling about the shed where we had taken refuge.

"Frogmen—down and under!" ordered Yiftah. The empty pitcher and bits of *peetah* would tell the Egyptians all they wanted to know. We remained under water as long as we could, swimming all the while, but human lungs don't have the endurance of metal ones; we had to surface. Sure enough, the soldiers saw us at once. They came running down to the water's edge, yelling and firing their guns. We went under again, changing direction, but we knew that the coast guard cutters and their frogmen would be summoned in a matter of minutes. For the moment we were safe, but where could we go?

We kept going, but, without our fins, we couldn't hope to cover any great distance. Anyone accustomed to fins would find swimming without them almost hopeless.

"Over there, fellows! Find shelter!" Yiftah pointed to a stone and earth embankment which jutted out from the beach into the water. We went under again, swimming hard now toward the embankment. Bullets kept flicking up the water all around us, but moving targets, in the water, are not easy to hit. Yiftah's orders were to get there in a roundabout way, to confuse the enemy. We knew exactly how this was to be done, but our lungs were having a hard time. At this point we could not think of surfacing, or else the enemy would easily know where we were headed. The soldiers would come running to the embankment—and that would be the end.

I think that we broke every record on the books for staying under water. Only when we were among the rocks, on the farther side of the embankment, did we surface. For a few moments we couldn't utter a sound. We hung on, gasping; our lungs were pounding as though they were a thousand drums.

Again we knew that we wouldn't be safe very long. Tough and well-trained as we were, there was little hope for escape. The boats and the frogmen would soon reach the area and comb every inch of it. Also, our wounds had opened from the exertion, and the salt water was searing our bodies. We were dead tired. My feet felt as if they didn't belong to me.

"Hey, fellows!" Buki called out suddenly. "Look over there! A cave!"

He was right. Between two large boulders at the base of the embankment we could see a dark opening. "I'll look it over," Buki said and was off. We waited for him, our hearts thumping hard with new hope. The opening could lead to an undersea cave, full of water, in which case it would be of no help at all.

I hadn't prayed since leaving Morocco, but I did this time, hard. "Oh, God, make it a large cave!".

Buki's head bobbed up out of the water, then his hand beckoned to us to come on. We hurried to the spot, went under and into the cave. My prayer, I discovered, had been answered, although not entirely. The cave was rather small, but there was a space of some sixteen inches between the level of the water and the ceiling of the cave. This, considering our situation, was good enough. We bunched up inside, with only our heads above water; the air inside was none too plentiful. Amos and Assaf went down to the bottom and came up with handfuls of long seaweed. This they hung from the stones at the mouth of the cave, hiding the entrance almost completely. We held on to the sides of the cave and waited.

The search we had been expecting was not long in coming. From the other side of the embankment came the roar of motor boats. Overhead, the soldiers' boots grated on the rough stones. They searched for a long time; at one point a shower of pebbles fell across the opening of the cave, as a soldier almost lost his footing overhead. Finally they left, but we knew that they would still be searching in the area.

We waited until it was as dark outside as it was within the cave. Yiftah led the way out. "We'll head for the open sea," he said, "then turn east a bit and south to the shore. Stick together."

Our muscles, cramped from the hours in the cave, didn't respond too well. To make matters worse, the sea grew rough. We swam slowly, painfully, and turned east in Yiftah's wake. Lights blinked on the shore. We headed for the darkest spot along the beach.

I heard the labored breathing of the others. Yossi was swimming not far from me. But it was not the Yossi I knew. Already back in the cave he behaved strangely, holding on to the rocks, eyes closed. His breath was now coming in whistles. Something was wrong with him.

"Yossi!" I called. "Yossi—are you all right? How are you feeling?"

"Like a hamburger—well-done," he tried to grin. I realized that the blows he had taken must have cost him a lot of blood. I swam over to his side and tried to prop him up, but carrying his weight and my own at the same time was beyond my strength.

"Let go," Yossi whispered, "or both of us will drown."

I had no intention of letting him go under. I supported him a bit, then one of the others took my place. Yossi kept talking, without making any sense.

We had no way of knowing that the submarine was waiting for us, at that very moment, at the bottom of the sea. Only later did we learn that its orders were to return to the spot every night and wait for us, until further instructions. If we had only known! But we didn't, and we kept on swimming, south, to what seemed to be a deserted spot on the beach. We pushed on, moving our limbs mechanically and feeling as though the next wave would be our last. I kept lowering my legs, hoping to touch something solid. Finally, as I was about to give up all hope, I felt the sand.

"Fellows," I yelled hoarsely. "We made it!"

We crawled up to the beach. There was no thought of caution or posting a guard. We were exhausted beyond belief. Our clothes were in shreds. We lay on the sand and fell asleep.

When I awoke, the thin crescent of the moon was already in the western sky. Not a sign of life showed anywhere on the beach. A few lights blinked in the distance.

"Yossi," I whispered to the figure sprawled next to me. The others were also stirring.

"Thanks, fellows," murmured Yossi faintly. "I would never have made it without you."

Yiftah was on his feet, looking around. "We must find a boat," he said curtly. "The open sea is our only chance."

The rough sea didn't look inviting, but we knew that Yiftah was right; the open sea *was* our only chance. Buki and Amos supported Yossi—one of his legs had given way—and we started out, plodding painfully through the sand.

"Hey, look there!" We saw a jeep, apparently abandoned during the air raid. "A gift from heaven," exclaimed Amos. "Let's go!"

We were even more surprised to find a key in the ignition lock, but the reason for it soon became clear. The motor wouldn't start, and the owner had probably gone to look for a repair man. I raised the hood and groped about. Now I was grateful to the instructor in that driving course who insisted that even a diver had to be familiar with motorized vehicles. I soon found the cause of the breakdown and, to the pitifully weak cheers of my companions, got in behind the wheel and started the motor. With everyone aboard, I drove the jeep to the hard-packed sand. Here the going was easier and less dangerous.

Some two miles farther to the east we came to a private boat basin. A trim sailboat was rocking gently at the small wooden wharf. The nearby house looked deserted; instead of taking the precaution of stopping some distance away I drove right up to the wharf.

"Min hadda? Who's there?" came a voice from the house, and lights went up inside.

"Hurry, fellows! Jump aboard!" ordered Yiftah.

With what must have been my last remaining bit of strength I leaped from the jeep on to the wharf and into the boat. Yiftah had already untied the mooring rope.

"Min hadda?" came the voice again. A shot rang out, then another. Amos, at my side, suddenly slumped down to the bottom of the boat.

"He's been hit," I cried. All of us dropped down to escape the whining bullets. Yiftah pushed the boat away from the wharf. Two of the fellows seized the oars, thrust them into the oarlocks and pushed hard. Slowly the boat moved out of the basin.

Amos was unconscious. Blood was flowing from his thigh, but his pulse was beating strongly. I tore up what was left of my shirt and bound the wound as best as I could, in the darkness.

Yiftah and Assaf lost no time putting up the sail. The brisk wind caught it, and we found ourselves skimming over the black sea. Home was still far away, but our stroke of luck, so far, had been so amazing that we were full of hope again. Luck—and the training we had received, hard and rigorous training which made nothing seem impossible.

"Water!" murmured Amos. We had none. Assaf moistened his lips with sea water.

Only four of us could hope to hold out much longer, without food or water. Had we known that our army was in control of the Gaza Strip we would have taken the much shorter route there. As it was, we had to keep away from the coast; the owner of the sailboat had no doubt gotten in touch with the Egyptian coast patrol.

When morning came we lowered the sail, to make discovery less likely, and continued rowing, under the scorching sun. Our thirst was the worst problem.

Yossi was running a high fever. We knew that unless help came very soon he wouldn't hold out. Amos was unconscious most of the time.

To the north, always to the north. At nightfall we hoisted sail again. The cool breeze revived us. We lay on the bottom of the boat, without moving.

When day dawned, I looked at my companions and was frightened by what my eyes beheld. They seemed to have shriveled up, and their lips were cracked frightfully from thirst. I closed my eyes, and orange circles began dancing around me. As from a distance I heard Gal calling me to come home—he was laughing, crying, calling . . .

I heard Yiftah's hoarse voice. He alone had the strength to sit up and work the rudder.

"Fellows," he croaked. "A ship! A destroyer! Looks like ours!"

I could only lift my head; the rest of my body seemed paralyzed. In the distance I saw a long, dark shape moving toward us. I shielded my eyes from the sun and looked again. We all looked. It was a destroyer—that we could see. It could be ours. But did it see us?

We tore the white sail off the mast, tied the strips to the oars and began signaling in code. We now had no sail. One of the oars fell from the tired grasp of the frogman holding it and slid into the sea. But what did it matter? We didn't have the strength any more to use it.

"They see us!" yelled Buki.

"They're coming! They're coming!" all of us yelled.

Evening. A light breeze was blowing across the water. We stood on the deck of the destroyer, and our eyes were on the eastern horizon. There lay Haifa and the Carmel slope, alive with lights—the lights of home, our native land! An eternity had passed since we had seen it last. We were still trembling with excitement, almost disbelieving our good fortune. The little transistor I was holding was broadcasting the most wonderful news imaginable—the capture of Sinai, the liberation of Jerusalem and the Western Wall, the seizure of the Golan Heights. Our troops were at Mt. Hermon, in Jericho, on the bank of the Suez Canal.

"I told you they'd be picking us up," said Yossi. He was relaxing in a deck chair, still weak and very pale but his smiling self again. "You heard what they said. The sub has been waiting for us there at night, and this boat has been looking for us by day. That's how important we are."

"Let's just say that the navy never gives up on its men," said Yiftah.

Yes, thanks to the navy and to the tough training it had given us we were still alive. We did the impossible, just as our forces did when they knocked out the Arab armies. Below, in the sick bay, Amos was resting, after a transfusion. We felt sure that he would pull through. Frogmen usually do.

Haifa Bay was before us, mirroring the lights on the Carmel. Yes, the war was over. I was going home—to

Dalit, to little Gal, to Father. I guess happy endings are found not only in story books; they happen in real life, too. I was glad that darkness hid the tears that were rolling down my stubbly cheeks.

I saw a shooting star. "Let there be no more war, only peace, peace! Peace!" I wanted to shout. But I was too shy. But quietly, as a real prayer should be uttered, I whispered into the wind: "Peace—let there be peace."